Introduction to
Lipids

Consulting Editor

P. SYKES, M.Sc., Ph.D.,
Fellow of Christ's College,
University of Cambridge

Other titles in the European Chemistry Series

BANWELL: Fundamentals of Molecular Spectroscopy
BARNARD: Theoretical Basis of Inorganic Chemistry
BARNARD & CHAYEN: Modern Methods of Chemical Analysis
BARNARD & MANSELL: Fundamentals of Physical Chemistry
BRENNAN & TIPPER: A Laboratory Manual of Experiments in Physical Chemistry
BU'LOCK: The Biosynthesis of Natural Products
HALLAS: Organic Stereochemistry
KEMP: Practical Organic Chemistry
SUTTON: Electronic Spectra of Transition Metal Complexes
WILLIAMS & FLEMING: Spectroscopic Methods in Organic Chemistry
WILLIAMS & FLEMING: Spectroscopic Problems in Organic Chemistry

Introduction to
Lipids

Dennis Chapman Ph.D., D.Sc.
Unilever Research Laboratory, Welwyn
Professor Associate in Chemistry
University of Sheffield.

McGRAW-HILL · LONDON
New York · Sydney · Toronto · Mexico · Johannesburg · Panama

Published by
McGRAW-HILL Publishing Company Limited, McGraw-Hill House,
MAIDENHEAD, BERKSHIRE, ENGLAND

94081

Printed and bound in Great Britain

Preface

Apart from the important advances made by lone individualists, such as Thudicum in his studies of the constitution of the brain in the late nineteenth century, by Hilditch and co-workers on the constitution of natural oils and fats in the twentieth century, and technological research on the glycerides and fatty acids inspired by industrial needs, for many years relatively little attention was given to the study of lipids.

Nowadays there is considerable interest in lipids, and scientists of many disciplines including biochemists, biophysicists, medical workers, plant and animal physiologists, are all studying, or are concerned with, various aspects of lipid chemistry. This considerable change in emphasis has occurred partly because of recent advances in separation and analytical methods, and partly because of the increased interest in the biological relevance of the polar lipids, special interest being focused on the role of phospholipids, sphingolipids, and glycolipids in membrane and lipoprotein structures. Interest has been stimulated by the possible relevance of dietary lipids to the growing incidence of coronary thrombosis in the population, and by the realization of the importance of the organizational properties of cell membranes in determining many of the cell's reactions.

As the details of the replication processes of the cell have been gradually revealed, attention has been increasingly drawn to problems associated with cell organization and membrane structure. The organization of chlorophyll in the chloroplast, of retinene in the eye, the activation of certain enzymes, the electron transport system in mitochondria, are all considered to arise from the architectural and organizational properties of the polar lipid molecules present in the membranes. The immunogenic properties of lipids, the study of demyelination, the rôle of lipids in the enhancement of the virulence of micro-organisms, and the rôle of lipids in determining brain function and brain diseases, are among the many other exciting active research areas at the present time.

The aim of this short text is to give a simple introduction for undergraduates and postgraduates at universities and other technical centres for an understanding of lipid molecules, to show their structure, synthesis and biosynthesis, and to show their biological relevance. General references are provided at the end of each chapter to provide an easy entry into the detailed and rather extensive scientific literature. Whilst the emphasis throughout is on the biological relevance of lipids, the early chapters on the fatty acids and glycerides may also be useful to those more interested in the industrial aspects of these molecules. The chapters on the complex polar lipids should be of value to those interested in the biochemical and biological aspects of these molecules.

A brief general discussion is included in the first chapter on the physical behaviour of lipid molecules, particularly in the presence of water. More detailed comments on the physical properties are also given in the later chapters. It is my firm opinion that a full understanding of the biological function of these molecules will rely very considerably on an understanding of the micellar and liquid-crystalline properties of these molecules. A great interest is being shown at the present time in physical studies of model membranes made with polar lipids, and I include some comments on this.

The scientific area encompassed in lipid research is now such a vast one that it is already clear that to understand completely the biological role of these molecules will require, in future years, many studies of an interdisciplinary nature.

The nomenclature of lipids is sometimes confusing. I have, therefore, included the generally accepted names and also, where possible, their scientifically correct names. As this text was going to press, new proposals by an IUPAC–IUB commission were published. I have included, for reference, a brief account of these new proposals in an Appendix.

It is hoped that this text will provide an easy first step for the newcomer who is interested in understanding the chemistry, biochemistry, and biophysics of lipids.

Acknowledgements

The writing of a book which requires an interdisciplinary approach, such as the present one, raises a number of difficulties; in particular one cannot expect to be an authority in all the different areas.

I wish, therefore, to acknowledge many helpful comments and discussions particularly with Dr D. Bowyer, Dr R. Aneja, Dr T. Grey, and Dr P. G. Fast on various sections of the book. I am also grateful for the secretarial assistance of Mrs J. Johnson. I also wish to acknowledge the patience of my wife Margaret and children Michael, Paul, and Alison during the work involved at home in the preparation of the book.

DENNIS CHAPMAN

Contents

1. General Introduction

There have been many attempts to define the scientific area encompassed by the term 'lipid'. Because the first attempts at definition were based mainly upon solubility considerations, at one time, molecules such as carotenoids and triterpenes were included within the classification. Thus lipids were considered to be substances which are insoluble in water, but soluble in solvents such as ether, chloroform, and benzene. Later definitions have laid less emphasis upon the solubility characteristics and are based upon the concept that lipid molecules are actual or potential derivatives of fatty acids or closely related substances. (This definition excludes cholesterol and other sterols but not the esters.)

In this chapter we shall start by describing the various classes of lipid molecules which we shall be discussing in more detail in the subsequent pages. These include fatty acids and waxes, the glycerides, the phosphoglycerides, sphingolipids, and also the more complex lipids including cerebrosides and sulphur lipids. As the polar lipids, such as the phospholipids, are considered to be bound in the cell into complexes with proteins, we shall also briefly mention the various types of lipoproteins which are known to occur. We shall also describe some general aspects of the physical chemistry of lipids which are important for an understanding of their behaviour and function.

The Major Lipid Classes

The fatty acids are the basic units of lipid molecules and markedly determine their properties. Free fatty acids occur naturally only in small quantities, e.g., the lower fatty acids such as acetic, butyric, and caproic occur in the free form in milk fats. At one time the free fatty acids detected in tissue extract were considered to arise from degradative actions occurring during the isolation procedures.

However, it has now been established that small quantities of free fatty acids are normal constituents of the tissue lipid pool.

In the majority of mammalian lipids the fatty acids are straight chain, even numbered, monocarboxylic acids. The most predominant of these are lauric, myristic, palmitic, and stearic acids. Small amounts of branched and odd numbered acids do occur naturally, but only in small percentages. Unsaturated acids also occur: these acids are particularly important, and monoenoic (oleic acid), dienoic (linoleic acid), trienoic (linolenic acid), and tetraenoic acid (arachidonic acid) are known. Linoleic acid is regarded as having particular biological importance and it and arachidonic acid have been called 'essential fatty acids'. An example of the structure of a commonly occurring saturated fatty acid is shown:

$$CH_3(CH_2)_{16}C\overset{\displaystyle O}{\underset{\displaystyle OH}{<}}$$

Stearic acid

Various other types of fatty acid occur and we shall discuss them further in chapter 2. The salts of the fatty acids, called soaps, are sometimes included in discussions of lipids but we shall not discuss them in detail in this text. (The physical properties of soap–water systems are analogous to the behaviour of some naturally occurring lipids, see page 11.)

Neutral lipids

The neutral (uncharged) lipids are amongst the most abundant natural fatty acid derivatives and they occur in both animal and plant tissues. The most predominant members of this class are the esters of the fatty acids with glycerol.

Glycerides. (Note that the groups indicated by R contain hydro-carbon chains and could also be drawn $\diagup\!\diagdown\!\diagup\!\diagdown\!\diagup\!\diagdown$, see page 10.)
$$R_1$$

$$
\begin{array}{l}
\text{CH}_2\text{OCOR}_1 \\
| \\
\text{R}_2\text{OCOCH} \\
| \\
\text{CH}_2\text{OCOR}_3
\end{array}
\qquad R_1, R_2, R_3 = \text{fatty alkyl groups}
$$

Triglyceride

In mammalian tissues triglycerides are present to the largest extent, but diglycerides and monoglycerides are also present in certain tissues.

A number of permutations and combinations of fatty acids on the glycerol residue are possible. Thus two different fatty acids can give rise to any one of six triglycerides, whilst three fatty acids can give eighteen triglycerides. A whole range of fatty acids is found to be associated with the natural triglycerides. The mode of distribution of these fatty acids is still not fully understood although many differing theories have been proposed.

The triglycerides are of considerable commercial importance and are used in the manufacture of foods, including margarine and chocolate.

Cholesterol and cholesterol esters. Glycerol is by far the major polyhydroxy alcohol found esterified to long-chain fatty acids in mammals, but another important alcohol which can be found in the esterified and unesterified form is cholesterol.

Cholesterol

This is the only *sterol* found associated with long-chain fatty acids in mammals. There is particular interest in cholesterol and its esters at the present time because of their possible relation to atherosclerosis. Cholesterol is found in large quantities in many cell membranes and in the brain.

Glyceryl ethers. The glyceryl ethers can be represented by the formula

$$\begin{array}{l} CH_2OR \\ HOCH \\ CH_2OH \end{array}$$

where R is usually palmityl, stearyl, or oleyl. Glyceryl ethers occur in marine animals, but only to a limited extent in land animals.

Fatty alcohols and waxes. Although not found to any significant extent in land mammals, the waxes occur in insects, aquatic animals, and certain plants. The sperm of whale contains considerable amounts of long-chain alcohols such as cetyl, stearyl, and oleyl alcohols, esterified with long-chain fatty acids. The waxes can be represented as carboxylic esters of the type:

$$RC \overset{\displaystyle O}{\underset{\displaystyle OR'}{\big\langle}}$$

where R and R' are long-chain alkyl groups. Natural leaf waxes contain alcohols such as myricyl alcohol $C_{30}H_{61}OH$ and myricyl palmitate occurs in high concentration in beeswax.

Phosphoglycerides. Phosphoglycerides are found in all cellular organisms. They are essential components of cell membranes and have been implicated in such processes as active transport, blood coagulation, diseases of the nervous system, cancer, and many other important biological processes which we shall discuss in chapter 4. The structure of the phosphoglycerides is shown:

$$\begin{array}{l} CH_2OCOR_1 \\ | \\ R_2OCO-C-H \\ |\qquad\quad O \\ |\qquad\quad || \\ CH_2OPOX \\ \qquad\quad | \\ \qquad\quad O^- \end{array} \qquad R_1R_2 \text{ fatty alkyl groups}$$

Typical phosphoglyceride

Various groups occur at position X giving rise to a wide range of derivatives. These derivatives include phosphatidylcholines (lecithins), phosphatidylethanolamines, phosphatidylserines, phosphatidylinositols, and phosphatidic acids which we shall discuss in chapter 4. In the various phosphoglycerides the nature of the fatty acids varies; a whole range of chain lengths, unsaturation, and branching is observed. Unsaturated fatty acids occur predominantly at the R_2 position shown in the structural formula.

Sphingolipids. The sphingolipids are characterized by the derivation of their members from a number of long-chain hydroxylic bases; sphingosine, dihydrosphingosine, phytosphingosine, and dehydrophytosphingosine. No glycerol is present. The first two bases occur in animal fats, particularly in pancreatic, brain, and spinal tissues. Sphingomyelin is a sphingosine-containing lipid.

$$CH_3(CH_2)_{12}CH=CH-\underset{\underset{\displaystyle COR_1}{\underset{\displaystyle |}{\overset{\displaystyle NH}{\underset{\displaystyle |}{}}}}{\overset{\displaystyle OH}{\underset{\displaystyle |}{CH}}}-\overset{OH}{\underset{|}{CH}}-CH_2O\overset{\overset{\displaystyle O}{\|}}{\underset{\underset{\displaystyle O^-(H, OH)}{|}}{P}}OCH_2CH_2\overset{+}{N}(CH_3)_3$$

R_1 = fatty alkyl chain

Sphingomyelin

There are a number of complex lipids which contain carbohydrate groupings. These include cerebrosides, gangliosides, and sulphur lipids. We shall discuss them in more detail in chapters 5 and 6. The cerebrosides contain galactose, a high molecular weight fatty acid, and sphingosine. Individual cerebrosides are differentiated by the kind of fatty acid in the molecule.

$$\underset{\underset{\displaystyle \underset{\displaystyle CH_2-O}{|}}{\underset{\displaystyle CHNHOCR}{|}}}{CH(OH)CH=CH(CH_2)_{12}CH_3}$$

R = alkyl group

Cerebroside

Gangliosides occur in the brain. They contain neuraminic acid as well as C_{22} or C_{24} fatty acids, sphingosine, and three molecules of a hexose (glucose and galactose). A hexosamine is sometimes substituted for neuraminic acid in some gangliosides.

Lipoproteins

In nature lipid molecules are often found to occur in association with proteins. Almost all biological membranes, such as cytoplasmic membranes, nuclear membranes, endoplasmic reticulum, cristae of mitochondria, lamellae of chloroplasts, myelin of nerve fibres, are composed of lipoproteins. The lipoproteins support the metabolic apparatus in mitochondria, the photosynthetic apparatus in chloroplasts, and are thought to be associated with enzymatic activity in mitochondria. Lipids and proteins also occur as lipoproteins in the nervous system. Various types of lipoprotein occur; there are those which are soluble in water and insoluble in organic solvents; some occur which are insoluble in water and in organic solvents and there is a third group which is insoluble in water and soluble in certain organic solvents. The latter group has been named the proteolipids.

Table 1.1. Composition of the major plasma lipoproteins*

Type	Peptide	Phospho-lipid	Cholesterol		Glycer-ide	Non-esteri-fied fatty acid
			Alcohol	Ester		
Chylomicrons	2·0	7·0	2·0	5·0	84·0	—
β-Lipoprotein (density 0·94–1·00)	8·0	18·0	7·0	14·0	50·0	2·0
β-Lipoprotein (density 1·03)	21·0	22·0	8·0	37·0	11·0	1·0
α-Lipoprotein (density 1·063–1·20)	50·0	22·0	3·0	14·0	8·0	3·0

* Oncley, J. L. in *Hormones in Human Plasma* (ed. H. N. Antoniades), p. 13, Little, Brown & Co. Boston, 1960.

All, or nearly all, of the lipid components in blood plasma are combined with proteins to form the so-called soluble lipoproteins. These lipoproteins are of three main groups, the alpha, beta-lipoproteins, and the chylomicrons (see Table 1.1). The soluble lipoproteins are considered to be responsible for the transport of lipids in blood. The nature of the bonding between lipid and protein is still not yet well understood, although there have been many speculations about this.

Analysis

Recent advances in separation and analytical techniques have now begun to make it possible to determine the detailed lipid composition of animal and plant tissues. As a particular tissue can contain various lipid classes the analysis is by no means straightforward. This is further complicated by the fact that, within each lipid class, there is a variety of chain lengths and unsaturation. Added to this is the complication of other groupings which can be present in the fatty acid chains such as cyclopentene, hydroxyl, or methyl groups.

The sampling procedures are, of course, a most vital part of the analysis of the tissues. A determined lipid composition may not necessarily be representative because with cell membranes the lipid composition of the different membranes of one cell type can vary, and there can be variations in lipid composition dependent upon the species and also upon environmental factors affecting the species.

The organelles must be isolated and freed from all contaminating matter if studies of specificity of lipid composition are required. The organelle may be characterized by means of electron microscopy to provide information on morphological integrity and this may be supplemented by enzyme assay. Post-mortem degradation has to be guarded against and can be prevented by rapidly cooling the organelles to low temperatures ($\sim 4°C$). This has been found to preserve lipid composition for periods of weeks and up to months prior to analysis.

The extraction of lipids from biological tissue is generally complicated by a number of factors. This is because (a) some lipids are linked with protein or carbohydrate and these complexes are usually insoluble in the normal lipid solvents such as ether, alcohol, and chloroform; (b) some lipids are only soluble in a limited range of these solvents; and (c) some non-lipid constituents of tissues are also dissolved by these solvents.

Generally there is no difficulty in extracting triglycerides from tissues such as adipose tissue or oil seeds. The triglycerides are not bound into lipoproteins or lipocarbohydrate complexes and they are easily soluble in the lipid solvents. Triglycerides can usually be extracted with successive uses of a solvent such as acetone which first extracts the water from the tissue and then the triglycerides themselves. Alternatively the tissue can be dried and extracted with any desired solvent.

Phospholipids, sphingolipids, and polar lipids are usually present in a bound form and, in this case, solvents such as methanol, ethanol, or acetone are used to break the linkages. Ethanol–ether and chloroform–methanol solvent systems are frequently used. Subsequently the solvent is removed from this extract of the wet tissue by a vacuum evaporation.

After washing this solution the total lipid is obtained by removing the solvent. It may then contain phospholipids, sphingolipids and simple lipids. Some contamination of the lipids can occur. The phospholipids in particular solubilize many non-lipid components such as sugars, free amino acids, sterols, urea, and many inorganic substances. These may be removed by special washing techniques or by chromatographic techniques using column or paper chromatography.

A number of techniques are used for the detailed fractionation of the lipids. These include countercurrent distribution methods, paper chromatography methods, and column chromatography.

Precise procedures for quantitative analysis of lipid composition involve the minimum handling of the lipid extracts to avoid decomposition and contamination. The most rapid modern procedures that are relatively precise now employ thin-layer chromatography (TLC). With this technique the process of analysis is as follows: Two-dimensional TLC with two different solvent systems is used for separation. The TLC spots are located and scraped or aspirated from the plates. The molar amounts of the lipid classes are next determined spectrophotometrically, e.g., phosphorus analysis for phospholipids, carbohydrate determination with anthrone or α-naphthol for glycolipids, trinitrobenzene sulphonic acid for lipids with free amino groups including sphingolipids after hydrolysis to release sphingosine, and a zinc chloride–acetyl chloride procedure for cholesterol. Sub-cellular organelle extracts usually contain sucrose or other substances added in the isolation procedure. The amounts are sufficiently large so that the spotting solutions may contain insoluble solids that interfere with sample application to the plate. These contaminants are removed by Sephadex column chromatography prior to TLC.* Finally the fatty acid composition of the small spots separated by TLC is determined by gas chromatography of fatty acid methyl esters. Quantitative gas phase chromatography is now routinely carried out on nanogram amounts of material.

Physical Chemistry

The lipids have a variety of unusual physical properties, some of which, such as their solid state properties, are of great technological importance, whilst others, such as their behaviour in water, are of considerable biological importance.

Solid state properties

In the solid state fatty acids, waxes, and glycerides exhibit the phenomenon of polymorphism, i.e., they exhibit multiple melting points. This phenomenon results from the fact that these molecules can occur in a variety of different crystal forms. Transformation from one polymorphic form to another can occur by either heating or cooling, or by crystallization from different solvents. The different forms display different X-ray diffraction patterns (i.e., different long or short spacings) and also different infrared spectra. The rheological properties of the polymorphic forms can differ greatly. This polymorphism arises either from the different ways, as seen in cross-section, in which the hydrocarbon chains can pack together, affecting the short spacings, or in the variation in the tilt of the hydrocarbon chains to the base of the molecule, see Fig. 1.1 which shows the same hydrocarbon chain at different angles of tilt and the different long spacings.

Some lipids, e.g., the phosphoglycerides, have other interesting solid state properties. These properties arise from the fact that melting of part of the molecule (the hydrocarbon chain region) can occur at much lower temperatures than the normal melting point. The

_____
* The use of adsorbents impregnated with silver nitrate in column and thin-layer chromatography enables the separation of compounds which only differ in amount, configuration, and/or position of the carbon–carbon double bonds.

The separation is based on complex formation of the Ag^+-ions with the π-electrons of the double or triple bond. This complex formation has been shown to be reversible, and equilibrium is reached very rapidly.

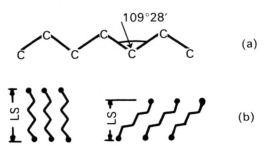

Fig. 1.1. *(a) Zig-zag carbon chain. (b) Long spacings of polymethylene chains*

thermal motion of the chains can be detected by methods such as i.r. and n.m.r. spectroscopy. The remaining crystallinity is due to the ionic interaction associated with the polar groups. The temperatures at which these transitions occur depend upon the presence or absence of unsaturation in the hydrocarbon chains of the lipid. When a *cis* group is present the liquid crystalline transition occurs at much lower temperatures than for the fully saturated lipid. The presence of water (see later) lowers the transition temperature to a limiting value (the Krafft temperature).

The behaviour of lipids in water

According to their behaviour at aqueous interfaces, lipids can be conveniently classified into two groups, polar lipids and non-polar lipids. This is simply a working classification as the distinction between these classes is not always a sharp one.

The non-polar lipid molecules remain associated and do not orient at interfaces. Examples of this type are the aliphatic hydro-carbons. Such substances are insoluble in the bulk phase and do not emulsify or suspend in water.

In the presence of water the polar lipids, e.g., fatty acids, phospho-glycerides, sphingolipids, etc., are oriented spontaneously with the polar groups in the surface of the water and the hydrocarbon chains above the surface. Monolayers of these molecules can be formed on a water surface.

The behaviour of surface-active molecules is often discussed in terms of the two opposing tendencies which exist within the same molecule. One part of the molecule is *hydrophilic*, i.e., it possesses an affinity for water,* whilst the remainder is *hydrophobic*, i.e., it has an antipathy for water. The word used to describe such molecules is *amphipathic*.

Dependent upon the hydrophobic-hydrophilic balance amphipathic molecules in water are (a) insoluble, (b) soluble, (c) swollen.

Micellar aggregation. At low concentrations, soluble amphipathic molecules can form solutions. The concentration at which molecular solubility is reached is termed the critical micellar concentration (c.m.c.). Above this concentration, aggregates of the molecules into spherical or rod-shaped particles occur; the hydrophobic tails of the molecules aggregate and form a particle with a liquid hydrocarbon centre; the ionic heads of the molecules project into the aqueous phase. Both the hydration and charge of the ionic heads of the molecule prevent coalescence of micelles and the separation into two phases. The molecules of the micelle are in rapid equilibrium both with the molecules in the free solution and with those of other micelles. With increased concentration of amphipathic molecules, more micelles are formed. The concentration of unassociated molecules remains constant or increases very slightly above the c.m.c. Micelle formation is characterized by a negative free energy which is the result of a large entropy factor and a small enthalpy term. Any amphipathic molecule above its c.m.c.—but below the concentration at which it forms a liquid crystalline phase—forms micelles spontaneously.

Liquid crystalline phases. As one progresses from a micellar solution to a more concentrated solution, the micelles probably grow from spheres into rods. This is suggested by a striking increase in the relative viscosity, and in a few cases has been proved by X-ray scattering measurements. At a certain concentration these rods become long and arrange themselves in a compact, hexagonal crystalline lattice. The solution, although still clear, becomes very viscous, and has marked birefringence under the polarizing microscope. This phase is called the 'middle soap' phase or hexagonal liquid-crystalline phase. It is made up of very long cylinders whose cross-section is identical in molecular arrangement to that of the spherical micelle. The cylinders are separated by water. At higher concentrations of lipid, a second type of liquid crystalline phase is formed which is much less viscous than the middle soap phase. This phase has a characteristic birefringence under polarized light and is

* When it is ionized a polar group becomes more hydrophilic.

lamellar in structure by X-ray diffraction. The lamellae consist of bimolecular leaflets of lipids separated by layers of water. Even with further dehydration of the lipid it continues to be liquid crystalline. At extremely low water concentrations it may, depending upon the temperature, become crystalline. The various structural arrangements which occur at different concentrations of lipid and water are illustrated in Fig. 1.2.

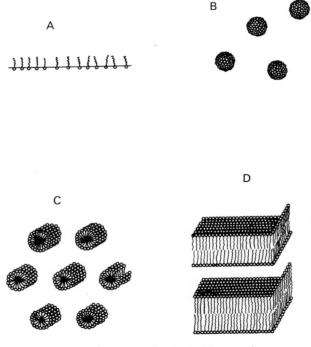

Fig. 1.2. *Various arrangements of polar lipids at various concentrations in water*
A—a monolayer at the air–water interphase
B—a micelle
C—a liquid crystalline phase of the hexagonal variety
D—a liquid crystalline phase of the lamellar variety

Below a certain temperature micelles will not form; the hydrocarbon chain of the amphipathic molecule are crystalline. If one heats a mixture of amphipathic molecules and water, the hydrocarbon chains melt over a narrow temperature range, allowing the water to enter the crystalline lattice and disperse the polar lipid as a micellar solution. Recooling the micellar solution results in a meta-stable gel; upon reheating, the gel transforms to a micellar solution at the same transition temperature. With lipids like the natural lecithins, the transition on heating is from the gel crystalline form to the liquid crystalline lamellar phase. Even at high dilution of lecithin in water, micelles are not observed. A phase diagram for a fully saturated lecithin–water mixture showing the Krafft temperature is given in Fig. 1.3.

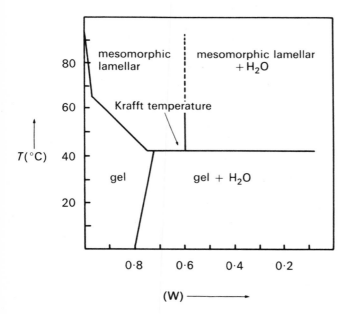

Fig. 1.3. A phase diagram for dipalmitoyl lecithin in water

The major factors influencing the Krafft temperature are (a) the energy required for water to penetrate the ionic crystal lattice, and (b) the energy required to melt the paraffin chains. The Krafft point is thus determined by the type of polar group, the counter-ions, and the nature of the paraffin chain. (The Krafft temperature of the salts of fatty acid soap varies with different cations.) The Krafft temperature rises with increasing chain length with a homologous series. The Krafft temperature of a *cis* unsaturated lipid is always below that of its *trans* stereo-isomer, and both are below that of a fully saturated homologue, cf. the solid state properties. Polar substitution or branching of the paraffin chain usually lowers the Krafft temperature.

A mixture of two amphipathic molecules may give a Krafft temperature which is intermediate between their respective Krafft transition temperatures.

In summary it is convenient to divide the polar lipid molecules into three groups according to their behaviour in water.

(a) *Insoluble* amphipathic molecules (lipids which do not interact with water in the bulk phase). Compounds of this group can orient at air–water and oil–water interfaces. However, they do not interact with water in the bulk phase and are invariably present in a separate liquid or solid phase. This group includes triglycerides, diglycerides, aliphatic alcohols, cholesterol or plant sterols, and fully protonated fatty acids.

(b) *Soluble* amphipathic molecules (polar lipids which have a finite molecular solubility in water), aggregate at higher concentrations and are strongly surface-active. Examples of this group are lysolecithin, phosphatidic acid, soaps, and ionic detergents. At low concentrations, such compounds form molecular solutions; at higher concentrations, micellar aggregation occurs. At still higher concentrations, the micelles coalesce into indefinitely long cylindrical aggregates; and finally, at very high concentrations, there is a phase transformation into a lamellar structure.

(c) *Swelling* amphipathic molecules (polar lipids which hydrate in water but remain associated). The compounds of this group are molecules with appropriately arranged polar and non-polar regions such that they hydrate in water yet remain associated. Water surrounds the polar heads of the molecules, yet their paraffinic chains, although liquid, remain closely associated by short-range forces. Since these phases have hydrodynamic and macroscopic liquid characteristics, yet have crystalline characteristics by X-ray analysis, the phases are termed liquid crystalline. The molecular arrangement may be lamellar, cylindrical or cubic. These phases are a property of many polar lipids, e.g., the lecithins, phosphatidylethanolamines, monoglycerides, glycol esters, and lipid extracts of myelin.

The hydrated liquid crystalline aggregates obtained with these lipids are easily dispersed in water, resulting in a milky liquid. Such a dispersion can be partially cleared by ultrasonification. The aggregates in such a cleared dispersion are sometimes called micelles. As the concentration of single molecules in the liquid is negligible (there is no c.m.c.) and probably no exchange of molecules between aggregates occurs, this term is not strictly correct. The term *micelloid* has been proposed for all non-covalently linked aggregates of this type.

Monomolecular films. Amphipathic compounds, soluble and insoluble, accumulate at interfaces in films which are mono-molecular. The surface tension or surface force—the tendency to keep the surface area at a minimum because of intermolecular forces—is reduced by this accumulation. Surface-active agents displace solvent molecules at the surface, and if techniques are used to measure the resistance to an increase in surface area, the surface agents act as if they expand the surface or exert a force in the opposite direction to the solvent molecules. This difference in the surface tension before and after the addition of a surface-active agent (per unit area) is termed the surface pressure.

Monomolecular films of insoluble or swelling amphipaths are prepared by spreading a solution prepared in a suitable solvent on a clean aqueous surface. These films are stable and the molecules do not pass into the bulk phase. The area of the film is varied by means of a barrier which sweeps the surface. It is usual to plot the surface pressure versus the area per molecule (in Å^2). The construction of such a force–area curve permits calculation of the cross-sectional molecular area at any given pressure. At a certain high pressure (the collapse pressure), the monolayer collapses giving the smallest possible surface area of the molecule. These monolayers can be studied and many force–area curves have been obtained with polar lipids. The presence of a *cis* unsaturated group in the hydrocarbon chain of the lipid produces *at a given temperature* a more expanded film than is obtained with the corresponding fully saturated compound, i.e., the unsaturated molecule occupies a greater area. With fully saturated polar lipids, at a given temperature, generally as the chain becomes shorter, the area occupied by the molecule becomes greater.

The potential difference across the air/water interface before and after the spreading of a monolayer can also be measured; this difference is termed the *surface potential*. Changes in the surface potential may be measured concomitantly with determination of the force–area curve and surface viscosity. Together, these data can provide information on the counter-ion binding and the charge interactions of the polar heads of the amphipathic molecules, as well as information concerning the interaction of the paraffin chains.

Other types of experiment are possible with these mono-molecular films. A *soluble* amphipathic molecule is injected beneath a film of an *insoluble* or *swelling* amphipath spread on water, and the change with time of the pressure (at fixed area) or area (at fixed pressure) is followed, while the surface potential and surface viscosity are recorded. Penetration reflects (a) the intrinsic surface activity of the *soluble* amphipathic molecule; (b) its interaction with the mono-molecular film, and (c) its interaction with the resultant mixed film.

The interpretations of these techniques are, however, not always straightforward; to what extent the results obtained with surface films can be applied to the behaviour of amphipathic molecules in bulk, and to what extent the monolayer is comparable to the bilayer, is still controversial.

Dispersion and solubilization. Dispersion is defined in the broadest sense as a solvent containing aggregates of any arrangement such that finite volume units have identical compositions. Micellar solutions, emulsions, and suspensions are all dispersions. The term, *solubilization* is used to describe the increased solubility of lipids observed in detergent solutions above their critical micellar concentration.

The liquid interior of the micelle is, in essence, a small sphere of hydrocarbon; insoluble lipids are partitioned between it and the aqueous phase. There is a marked increase in solubility which begins at the c.m.c. and increases with polar lipid concentration. A technique of 'dye solubilization' for measurement of the c.m.c. is based on the marked increase in dye solubility observed when micellar aggregation occurs.

Polar lipids are also 'solubilized' but these molecules inter-digitate, their polar groups facing the water. An alteration in micellar structure occurs generally by an increase in micellar size. With the further addition of an appropriate additive, a liquid crystalline phase of amphipathic molecule, additive, and water forms; the system becomes viscous and anisotropic. This system contains three components, the composition of any mixture (in weight percentage) is stated by a single point if triangular co-ordinates are used. The phases existing at different compositions are thus indicated by ternary phase diagrams. An example of a phase diagram of this type with lecithin, cholesterol, and water is given in chapter 4, see Fig. 4.20. Solubilization is also frequently used to describe the transformation of an opalescent solution to a clear solution. The human eye is an imperfect light-scattering apparatus, and this results in arbitrary definitions of solubility. With compounds such as lecithin or monoglycerides which form lamellar aggregates in water, the addition of appropriate surfactants such as bile salts reduces the size of the aggregates to such a point that they do not scatter visible light.

Lipids in organic solvents

Part of the early definition of lipids was that lipids are those substances which are insoluble in water but soluble in 'fat solvents' such as ether, chloroform, and benzene. Phospholipids, as opposed to triglycerides, are usually considered to be acetone insoluble; lecithins are considered to be soluble in alcohol, while phosphatidylethanolamines or phosphatidylserines are not. Sphingomyelins and cerebrosides are insoluble in ethyl ether. These generalizations, although useful, are not fully correct. The solubility of a given polar lipid in organic solvents depends markedly on the chain length and the degree of unsaturation (in other words on the hydrophobic–hydrophilic balance). The lecithins with hydrocarbon chain length of less than ten carbon atoms are very soluble in acetone whereas the higher members are not. Similarly, the solubility of lecithins in alcohol decreases considerably as the length of chain increases. This effect of chain length and unsaturation on lipid solubility has to be remembered when separation and analysis of different lipid classes are being carried out. The solubility of a given lipid may also be affected by the presence of other types of lipid.

In polar solvents such as ethanol, phospholipids are monomeric; in non-polar solvents such as benzene, however, they form micellar aggregates of large molecular weight ($\sim 50,000$). In this case the polar groups are considered to be in the interior and the hydrocarbon chains on the exterior of the micelle. This is the opposite situation to that which occurs in water.

Further reading

A. W. Ralston, *Fatty Acids and their Derivatives.* Wiley & Sons Inc., New York, 1948.

H. J. Deuel, *The Lipides*, Vol. I. *Chemistry.* Interscience, 1951.

K. Bloch (ed.), *Lipid Metabolism.* Wiley & Sons Inc., New York, 1960.

D. J. Hanahan, *Lipide Chemistry.* Wiley & Sons Inc., New York, 1960.

G. B. Ansell and J. N. Hawthorne, *Phospholipids. Chemistry, Metabolism and Function.* Elsevier Publishing Co., Amsterdam, 1964.

D. Chapman, *The Structure of Lipids by Spectroscopic and X-ray Techniques.* Methuen, London, 1966.

A. F. Hoffman and D. M. Small, *Ann. Rev. of Medicine*, **18**, 333, 1967.

2. Fatty Acids

Structure and Occurrence

Although fatty acids occur in small quantities in the free state in nature, they are found to occur primarily as essential components of many other lipid molecules. They are readily obtained by the hydrolysis of lipids such as the glycerides and phosphoglycerides. The fatty acids associated with these molecules are usually found to have a distribution of chain lengths, unsaturation or branching and only very occasionally are tissues observed which contain predominantly a single fatty acid.

The saturated fatty acids most commonly occurring in nature contain an even number of carbon atoms. Only small quantities of fatty acids containing an odd number of carbon atoms occur. Stearic (octadecanoic) acid is a very commonly occurring acid of the fully saturated type, whilst oleic acid (octadecenoic) is the most common of all fatty acids in nature. This acid has a *cis* unsaturated grouping in the chain. (This grouping causes the chain to 'kink'.) Other isomers of octadecenoic acid are known in which the double bond is situated in a different position along the chain from that observed with oleic acid. Some of these isomeric acids, e.g., petroselinic acid, occur naturally.

Many of the fatty acids are better known by their trivial names rather than by the systematic nomenclature and this can be rather confusing. The systematic nomenclature for fatty acids is based upon recommendations of the Geneva convention. The name of a saturated fatty acid is derived from that of the related hydrocarbon with the same number of carbon atoms.

For indicating the position of unsaturation the carbon atoms are numbered from the carboxyl carbon which is labelled 1. When Greek letters are used this carbon atom is not designated, the adjacent carbon atom is designated α; the last carbon atom in a chain is sometimes indicated by ω. The use of numbers is preferred but both methods are illustrated here for octanoic acid.

8	7	6	5	4	3	2	1
CH_3	CH_2	CH_2	CH_2	CH_2	CH_2	CH_2	CO_2H
$(\omega)\eta$	ζ	ε	δ	γ	β	α	
CH_3	CH_2	CH_2	CH_2	CH_2	CH_2	CH_2	CO_2H

The correct name for oleic acid is therefore octadec-*cis*-9-enoic acid, whilst the correct name for elaidic acid is octadec-*trans*-9-enoic acid. Based on the simple basic structure of the fatty acid, a large number of possible structures can occur.

Various types of unsaturation occur in natural fatty acids and these are shown in Table 2.1. The structures of some commonly occurring fatty acids are shown in Fig. 2.1. The trivial names, the scientific names and the usual abbreviations are shown.

Table 2.1. Types of unsaturation found in naturally occurring aliphatic compounds

Type of bond	Formulae
Isolated *cis*-double bond	$\begin{array}{c} R_1 \qquad\quad R \\ \diagdown \qquad \diagup \\ C{=}C \\ \diagup \qquad \diagdown \\ H \qquad\quad H \end{array}$
Isolated *trans* double bond	$\begin{array}{c} R_1 \qquad\quad H \\ \diagdown \qquad \diagup \\ C{=}C \\ \diagup \qquad \diagdown \\ H \qquad\quad R \end{array}$
2-Methyl-substituted carbonyl-conjugated double bond	$HO{-}\underset{\underset{O}{\parallel}}{C}{-}\underset{\underset{CH_3}{\mid}}{C}{=}CH{-}\underset{\underset{CH_3}{\mid}}{CH}{-}$
Methylene-interrupted double bonds (skipped diene)	$R{-}CH{=}CH{-}CH_2{-}CH{=}CH{-}R_1$
Conjugated double bonds	$R{-}CH{=}CH{-}CH{=}CH{-}R_1$
Conjugated triene	$R{-}CH{=}CH{-}CH{=}CH{-}CH{=}CH{-}R_1$
Allenic	$R{-}CH{=}C{=}CH{-}R_1$ 2 optically active forms
Acetylenic	$R{-}C{\equiv}C{-}R_1$

$$CH_3(CH_2)_{16}C\underset{OH}{\overset{O}{<}}$$

Stearic acid 18:0
(Octadecanoic acid)

$$CH_3(CH_2)_7CH=CH(CH_2)_7C\underset{OH}{\overset{O}{<}}$$

Oleic acid 18:1
(Octadec-9-enoic acid)

$$CH_3(CH_2)_4CH=CHCH_2CH=CH(CH_2)_7C\underset{OH}{\overset{O}{<}}$$

Linoleic acid 18:2
(Octadeca-9:12-dienoic acid)

$$CH_3CH_2CH=CHCH_2CH=CHCH_2CH=CH(CH_2)_7C\underset{OH}{\overset{O}{<}}$$

Linolenic acid 18:3
(Octadeca-9:12:15-trienoic acid)

$$CH_3(CH_2)_4CH=CHCH_2CH=CHCH_2CH=CHCH_2CH=CH(CH_2)_3C\underset{OH}{\overset{O}{<}}$$

Arachidonic acid 20:4
(Eicosa-5:8:11:14-tetraenoic acid)

Fig. 2.1. The structures of a range of naturally occurring fatty acids

Other variations on the fatty acid structure include the presence of a cyclopropane ring, e.g., lactobacillic acid, present in certain bacteria, contains this grouping, and a cyclopentene ring which occurs in hydnocarpic, chaulmoogric and gorlic acids whose structures are shown in Fig. 2.2.

The waxes present in tuberculosis, leprosy, and diphtheria bacilli contain branched chain acids such as tuberculostearic acid, phthioic

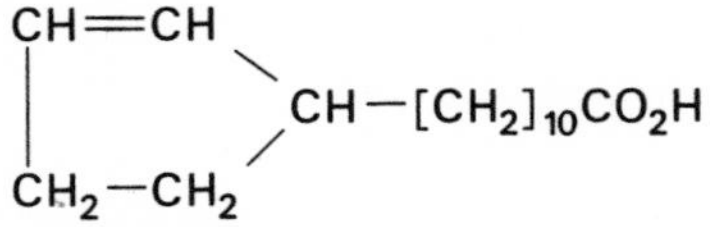

$$CH=CH$$
$$|$$
$$CH-[CH_2]_{10}CO_2H$$
$$CH_2-CH_2$$

Hydnocarpic acid

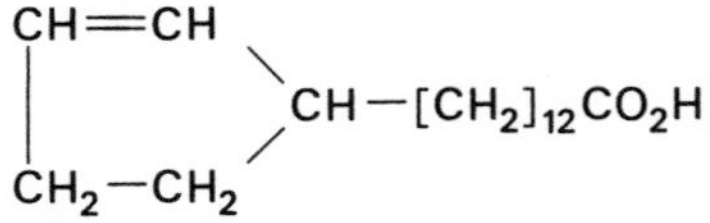

$$CH=CH$$
$$|$$
$$CH-[CH_2]_{12}CO_2H$$
$$CH_2-CH_2$$

Chaulmoogric acid

$$CH=CH$$
$$|$$
$$CH-[CH_2]_6CH=CH[CH_2]_4CO_2H$$
$$CH_2-CH_2$$

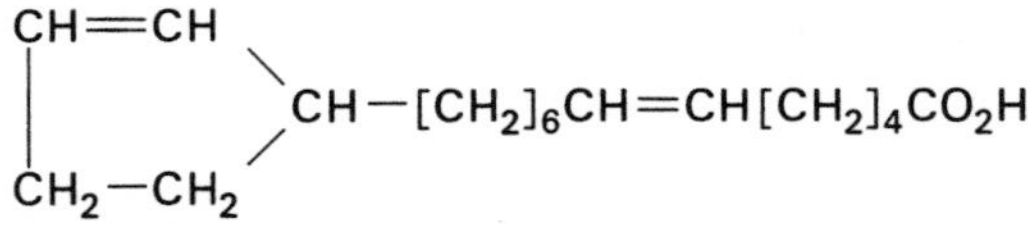

Gorlic acid

Fig. 2.2. The structures of some cyclopentene fatty acids

acid, and the mycolic acids. The mycolic acids are β-hydroxy acids which have a long aliphatic chain in the α-position. This includes the mycolic acids of the mycobacteria which have about 80 carbon atoms, the nocardic acids of about 50 carbon atoms, and the corynomycolic acids of Corynebacteria of about 32 carbon atoms (see Fig. 2.3).

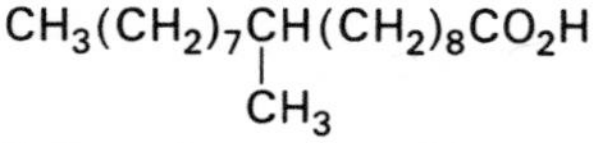

$$CH_3(CH_2)_7CH(CH_2)_8CO_2H$$
$$|$$
$$CH_3$$

Tuberculostearic acid

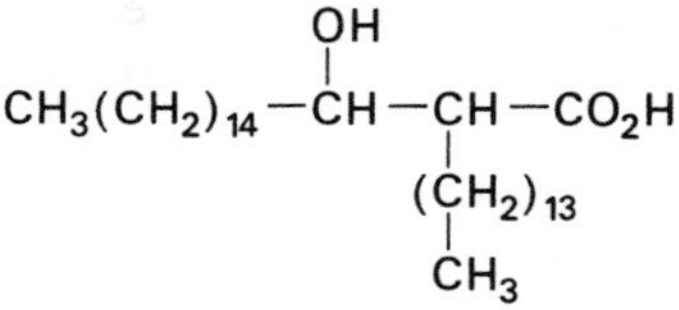

$$OH$$
$$|$$
$$CH_3(CH_2)_{14}-CH-CH-CO_2H$$
$$|$$
$$(CH_2)_{13}$$
$$|$$
$$CH_3$$

Corynomycolic acid

$$OH$$
$$|$$
$$CH_3(CH_2)_m-CH-CH-CH_2-CH-CHOH-CH-CO_2H$$
$$| | |$$
$$R \quad (CH_2)_{n_1}-CH_3 \ (CH_2)_{n_1}-CH_3$$

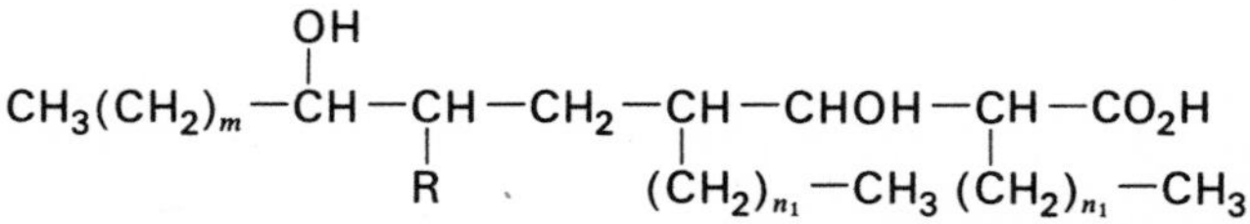

Mycolic acid (where $m \approx 17$, $n_1 = 21$ and 23 and R = an alkyl group)

Fig. 2.3.

The presence of double bonds, triple bonds, and sometimes hydroxyl groups, leads to considerable chemical reactivity, such as oxidation, reduction and the formation of various addition compounds. Some of the common derivatives of these reactions which occur with a mono unsaturated group are illustrated in Fig. 2.4.

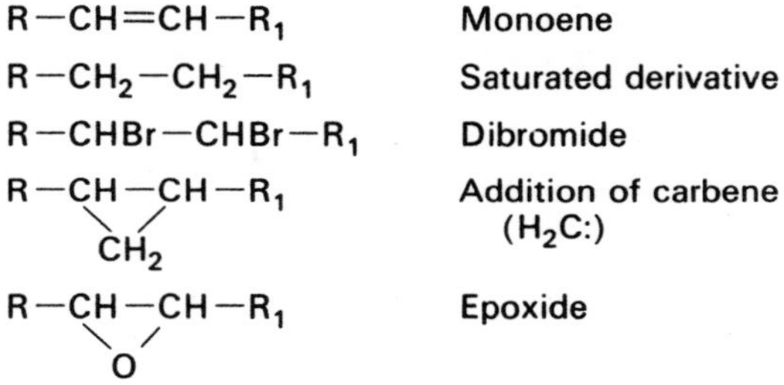

$$R-CH=CH-R_1 \qquad \text{Monoene}$$

$$R-CH_2-CH_2-R_1 \qquad \text{Saturated derivative}$$

$$R-CHBr-CHBr-R_1 \qquad \text{Dibromide}$$

$$R-\underset{\underset{CH_2}{\diagdown\diagup}}{CH}-CH-R_1 \qquad \begin{array}{l}\text{Addition of carbene}\\ \quad (H_2C\!:)\end{array}$$

$$R-\underset{\underset{O}{\diagdown\diagup}}{CH}-CH-R_1 \qquad \text{Epoxide}$$

Fig. 2.4. Some commonly encountered derivatives of ethylenic compounds (monoenes)

The amount of reactivity increases with the number of reactive sites present in the molecule.

The reaction of a pentadiene system, such as occurs in linoleic acid, is illustrated in Fig. 2.5. The methylene group between the double bonds is 'activated' and adds oxygen readily to form a hydroperoxide. Treatment of the hydroperoxide with alkali leads, via free radicals, to a double bond shift. The final result is a mixture of acids with conjugated double bonds. This reaction is the basis for the alkali isomerization technique, see page 38, used in the determination of polyunsaturated acids of the methylene interrupted type.

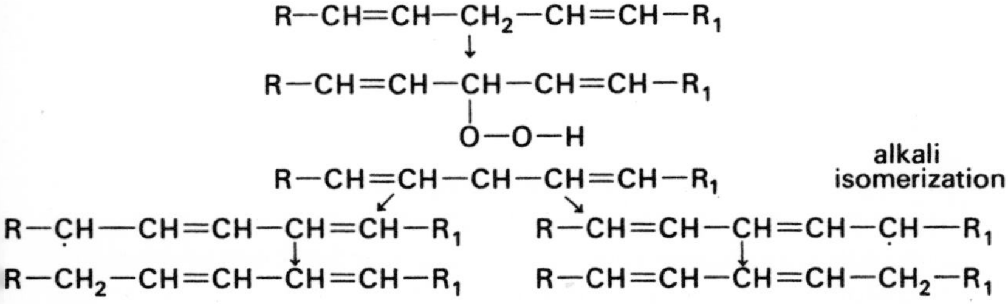

$$R-CH=CH-CH_2-CH=CH-R_1$$
$$\downarrow$$
$$R-CH=CH-CH-CH=CH-R_1$$
$$|$$
$$O-O-H$$

alkali isomerization

$$R-CH=CH-CH-CH=CH-R_1$$

$$R-\overset{.}{C}H-CH=CH-CH=\overset{.}{C}H-R_1 \qquad R-\overset{.}{C}H=CH-CH=CH-\overset{.}{C}H-R_1$$
$$R-CH_2-CH=CH-\overset{.}{C}H=CH-R_1 \qquad R-CH=CH-\overset{.}{C}H=CH-CH_2-R_1$$

Fig. 2.5. Reactions of the 'pentadiene' system

Chemical Synthesis of Fatty Acids

Several methods are now available for the synthesis of fatty acids and, in recent years, monoethenoid, polyethenoid, acetylenic, and branched chain acids have been prepared in addition to the relatively easily made acids of the saturated straight-chain type. These methods may be classified into three types (a) those involving no change in carbon chain length, (b) carbon-chain extension and (c) condensation reactions.

(a) No change in carbon chain length

This method involves chemical modification of naturally occurring long-chain compounds and includes (i) oxidation of alcohols and aldehydes, (ii) dehydration of hydroxy acids, (iii) dehydrohalogenation and dehalogenation of halogen-substituted acids, and (iv) the most important, hydrogenation of unsaturated acids. The method is of limited applicability because of the difficulty of isolating pure long-chain compounds, but a good example of its use is the preparation of stearic acid by the complete hydrogenation of mono- or polyethenoid C_{18} acids. α-β-Unsaturated acids can be prepared by the dehydrobromination of α-bromo acids, for example:

$$RCH_2CH_2CO_2H \xrightarrow{P/Br_2} RCH_2CHBrCO_2H \xrightarrow{PhNEt_2} RCH{=}CHCO_2H$$

Acetylenic acids may be obtained from ethylenic acids by bromination and subsequent dehydrobromination of the vicinal dibromo acid, thus:

$$CH_3(CH_2)_5CHOHCH_2CH{=}CH(CH_2)_7CO_2H \xrightarrow{Br_2} CH_3(CH_2)_5$$
$$cis$$
$$CHOHCH_2CHBrCHBr(CH_2)_7CO_2H$$
$$\xrightarrow{KOH} CH_3(CH_2)_5CHOHCH_2C{\equiv}C(CH_2)_7CO_2H$$

(b) Carbon-chain extension

Although methods using chain degradation are available for preparative purposes, degradation reactions are generally reserved for structure determination, and the main synthetic methods involve chain extension. Several routes have been developed for increasing the chain by either one or several carbon atoms.

The classical approach is the well-known homologenation process exemplified as follows:

$$RCO_2H \longrightarrow RCO_2R' \longrightarrow RCH_2OH \longrightarrow RCH_2X \longrightarrow$$
$$\longrightarrow RCH_2CN \longrightarrow RCH_2CO_2H$$

Alternative routes from the alkyl halide are provided by (i) reaction of the derived Grignard reagent with carbon dioxide, or (ii) reaction of the halide with malonic ester. The latter pathway increases the carbon chain by two atoms.

(i) $RBr \longrightarrow RMgBr \xrightarrow{CO_2} RCO_2H$

(ii) $RBr + CH_2(CO_2Et)_2 \longrightarrow RCH(CO_2Et)_2$
$$\longrightarrow RCH(CO_2H)_2 \longrightarrow RCH_2CO_2H$$

A modern development is the Arndt–Eistert synthesis, illustrated as

$$RCO_2H \longrightarrow RCOCl \xrightarrow{CH_2N_2} RCOCHN_2 \longrightarrow RCH_2CO_2H$$

Acetylenic compounds are now being used extensively for the synthesis of several types of fatty acid. The method may be illustrated in its simplest form as:

$$RC{\equiv}CNa \xrightarrow{CO_2} RC{\equiv}CCO_2Na \xrightarrow{H^+} RC{\equiv}CCO_2H$$

Alternatively, either the sodio-acetylene or a Grignard complex may be condensed with an α-ω dihalogeno compound.

The important oleic and linoleic acids have been synthesized by this method. See Fig. 2.6.

$$CH_3(CH_2)_7-C{\equiv}CH + I-(CH_2)_7-Cl$$
$$\quad\quad\quad\quad I \quad\quad\quad\quad\quad\quad II$$

$$\xrightarrow[\text{liq. NH}_3]{\text{NaNH}_2} CH_3(CH_2)_7-C{\equiv}C-(CH_2)_7-Cl$$
$$\quad\quad\quad\quad\quad\quad\quad III$$

$$\xrightarrow[\text{C}_2\text{H}_5\text{OH}]{\text{NaCN}} CH_3(CH_2)_7-C{\equiv}C-(CH_2)_7-CN$$
$$\quad\quad\quad\quad\quad\quad\quad IV$$

$$\xrightarrow{\text{hydrolysis}} CH_3(CH_2)_7-C{\equiv}C-(CH_2)_7-CO_2H$$
$$\quad\quad\text{stearolic acid} \quad\quad V$$

$$\xrightarrow[\text{C}_2\text{H}_5\text{OH}]{\text{Raney Ni}} \xrightarrow[\text{hydrogenation}]{\text{partial}} \overset{\text{cis}}{CH_3(CH_2)_7-CH{=}CH-(CH_2)_7-CO_2H}$$
$$\quad\quad\quad\quad\quad\quad\quad\quad\quad\quad\text{oleic}$$
$$\quad\quad\quad\quad\quad\quad\quad\quad\quad\quad\text{acid}$$

Fig. 2.6. *Synthesis of oleic acid*

An important method, known as anodic synthesis, has been developed in recent years and is based on the well-known Kolbe electrolytic reaction. In the adaptation for fatty acid synthesis a half-ester of a dicarboxylic acid is electrolysed with a monobasic acid and homologation by two to eight carbon atoms may be carried out in one step. The preparation of stearic acid from myristic acid is illustrated:

$$C_{13}H_{27}CO_2H + HO_2C(CH_2)_4CO_2CH_3$$
$$\downarrow$$
$$C_{13}H_{27}(CH_2)_4CO_2CH_3 + C_{13}H_{27} . C_{13}H_{27} + (CH_2)_8(CO_2CH_3)_2$$
$$\downarrow$$
$$CH_3(CH_2)_{16}CO_2H$$

(c) Condensation reactions

Early work on the condensation of comparatively small units to form long-chain compounds involved the reaction of acetoacetic ester with an alkyl halide and condensation of the product with a carbethoxyacyl halide to form a product (I) which, on careful hydrolysis, gives the keto acid (II). The method has been refined and

$$CH_3(CH_2)_6 . \overset{\displaystyle CO_2Et}{\underset{\displaystyle COCH_3}{C}} CO(CH_2)_8CO_2Et \longrightarrow CH_3(CH_2)_7CO(CH_2)_8CO_2H$$

I   II

extended; notably by the use of malonic ester in place of aceto-acetic ester and benzyl instead of ethyl esters. These reactants avoid the difficult hydrolysis step which generally results in a mixture of products. The keto acid (II) can be reduced to the saturated acid by the Clemmensen or Wolff–Kishner reaction.

Organo–metallic compounds have been applied to fatty acid synthesis and have the advantage that branched-chain compounds may be prepared. The method involves the condensation of an ethoxycarbonylacyl-halide with an organo–metallic compound, generally zinc or cadmium, for instance:

$$R_2Cd + ClCO(CH_2)_nCO_2C_2H_5 \longrightarrow RCO(CH_2)_nCO_2C_2H_5$$

Several modifications of this synthesis have been devised and a wide range of compounds has been prepared.

It is hoped that this very brief and simplified description of the chemical synthesis of fatty acids will serve as a useful introduction to the subject.

Oxidation of Fatty Acids

The oxidative degradation of fatty acids is a universal biochemical capacity among living organisms. In mammals, such oxidation occurs in a variety of tissues, including liver, kidney, and heart. Intracellularly, fatty acid oxidation occurs principally in the mitochondria.

The essential features of the pathway for oxidation of fatty acids were clearly detailed by Knoop in 1904. Nearly fifty years were required before the conclusions of Knoop received full experimental confirmation. Knoop arrived at the theory of 'β-oxidation' through feeding experiments employing fatty acids labelled in the terminal position with phenyl groups. He examined the end products in the urine of the experimental animals. When the animals were fed ω-phenyl fatty acids containing an even number of carbons in the straight chain, the end product in the urine was phenylaceturic acid, formed by the condensation of phenylacetic acid and glycine *in vivo*.

$$CH_2CO_2H + H_2N-CH_2-CO_2H \longrightarrow CH_2-\overset{O}{\overset{\|}{C}}-\overset{H}{\overset{|}{N}}CH_2CO_2H$$

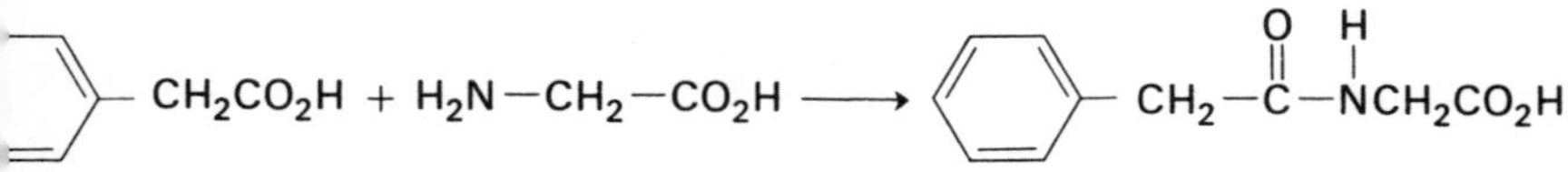

Phenylaceturic acid

In contrast, when similarly labelled fatty acids containing an odd number of carbon atoms were fed, the end product in the urine was hippuric acid, formed by condensation of benzoic acid and glycine *in vivo*.

$$CO_2H + H_2N-CH_2CO_2H \longrightarrow \overset{O}{\overset{\|}{C}}-\overset{H}{\overset{|}{N}}CH_2CO_2H$$

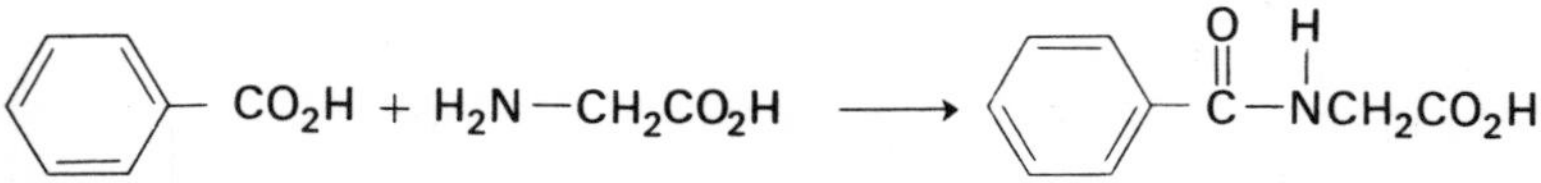

Hippuric acid

These are the results one would expect if the fatty acids are degraded by successive removal of two-carbon fragments from the parent molecule. The β-oxidation theory is shown in Fig. 2.7.

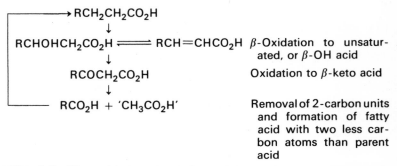

Fig. 2.7. *The oxidative metabolism of fatty acids according to the β-oxidation theory*

A difficulty in the early ideas was to account for the production of acetoacetate and other 'ketone bodies', such as hydroxybutyrate and acetone (which arise from acetoacetate), in the course of fatty acid oxidation.

The key discoveries in the understanding of the pathway of fatty acid oxidation were (a) the observation of fatty acid oxidation in cell-free preparations from the guinea pig liver, and (b) the elucidation of the structure of 'activated' fatty acids as the S-acyl derivatives of coenzyme A by Lynen and Reichert in 1951. The use of cell-free preparations permitted the identification of the individual enzymes involved in fatty acid oxidation and the determination of the properties of the catalytic reactions. The discovery of the acyl derivatives of CoASH showed why it had not been possible to detect any postulated intermediates, or any free short-chain fatty acids in the course of oxidation of longer molecules. The intermediates, including the short-chain fatty acids formed in the course of oxidation, occur only as the acyl-SCoA derivatives.

The general pathway for the oxidation of fatty acids in all organisms is indicated in Fig. 2.8. The parent fatty acid is activated by conversion to the fatty acyl-SCoA, oxidized to the α,β-unsaturated compound, hydrated, oxidized to the β-keto derivative, and finally subjected to a thiolytic cleavage yielding acetyl-SCoA and the fatty acyl-SCoA containing two less carbon atoms, which, in turn, undergoes the same series of reactions.

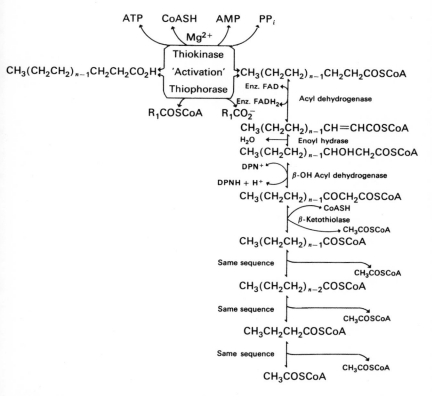

Fig. 2.8. *The pattern of fatty acid oxidation (after Markley, 1963)*

(FAD = Flavine-adenine dinucleotide, DPN$^+$ = diphosphopyridine nucleotide)

Ketone bodies, acetoacetate, β-hydroxybutyrate, and acetone, accumulate in the blood under certain abnormal conditions, e.g., diabetes. Each of these substances arises from the metabolism of acetoacetyl-SCoA. The principal fate of acetoacetyl-SCoA in the liver is conjugation with acetyl-SCoA, yielding β-hydroxy-β-methyl glutaryl-SCoA, an important precursor of cholesterol

$$CH_3\overset{O}{\underset{\|}{C}}-CH_2-\overset{O}{\underset{\|}{C}}-SCoA + CH_3\overset{O}{\underset{\|}{C}}-SCoA \longrightarrow$$

$$HO_2C-CH_2-\overset{CH_3}{\underset{OH}{\underset{|}{\overset{|}{C}}}}--CH_2-\overset{O}{\underset{\|}{C}}-SCoA + HSCoA$$

Under normal conditions, virtually all of this intermediate is channelled into cholesterol synthesis.

The sequence of reactions detailed for the oxidation of even-numbered fatty acids is also applicable to the oxidation of those with an odd number of carbon atoms. The main distinction between the two pathways lies in the products. The terminal cleavage of acetoacetyl-SCoA yields two molecules of acetyl-SCoA, while that of β-ketovaleryl-SCoA yields one of acetyl-SCoA and one of propionyl-SCoA. Further metabolism of propionyl-SCoA may occur via any of three general reaction paths.

Alternative routes for fatty acid oxidation

The β-oxidation scheme accounts for the major portion of oxidative reactions of the fatty acids. In addition to β-oxidation, α-oxidation and ω-oxidation yield products of some metabolic importance.

α-Hydroxy fatty acids, constituents of certain complex brain lipids, arise by the direct hydroxylation of preformed long-chain fatty acids. It has been shown that this reaction is an intermediate step in the formation of odd-numbered long-chain fatty acids. Oxidation of the α-hydroxy acids to the α-keto acids, followed by oxidative decarboxylation, yields these products. Such a pathway is in accord with the results of isotope labelling experiments concerned with synthesis of long-chain, odd-numbered fatty acids.

$$R-\overset{OH}{\underset{H}{\underset{|}{\overset{|}{C}}}}-CO_2H \longrightarrow R-\overset{O}{\underset{\|}{C}}-CO_2H \longrightarrow RCO_2H + CO_2$$

The ω-oxidation of fatty acids, yielding the dicarboxylic acids as products, has been known since 1932. Recent studies have dealt with the pathway for such reactions from mammalian and microbial sources. The ω-oxidation in both cases proceeds via a two-step pathway involving the intermediate formation of the ω-hydroxy fatty acid. In the system from mammalian liver, the hydroxylation requires oxygen and NADPH and is catalysed by microsomal preparations. In micro-organisms, the reaction also requires oxygen and NADPH but also exhibits a requirement for ferrous ions and occurs with the participation of at least two enzymes from the soluble portion of the cell. Oxidation of the ω-hydroxy fatty acids to the dicarboxylic acids requires NAD^+ and one or more enzymes from the soluble portion of the cell.

Biosynthesis of Fatty Acids

In the late 1950's clarification of the mechanism of fatty acid oxidation led to speculation on the means by which reversal of fatty acid oxidation might accomplish the net synthesis of fatty acids. However, a number of discoveries showed the unique nature of the biosynthetic pathway.

(a) The discovery of malonyl CoA led to the realization that not acetyl CoA, but the carboxylated derivative of acetyl CoA, was the 'C_2' unit in fatty acid biosynthesis in animals, plants and bacteria.

(b) The studies of a number of research groups showed that the $D(-)$-β-hydroxy acids and TPN, rather than the $L(+)$-β-hydroxy acids and DPN utilized in fatty acid oxidation, are involved in fatty acid synthesis.

(c) The discovery and subsequent characterization of the acyl carrier (protein) made it clear that this 'protein derivative' of coenzyme A, rather than CoA, is the thioester compound to which all of the intermediates in fatty acid synthesis in the bacteria are linked. Suggestive, but incomplete, evidence that a similar protein is involved in fatty acid biosynthesis in plants and animals has been reported.

Saturated fatty acids

The biosynthesis of saturated, straight chain, even-numbered fatty acids occurs in animal tissues and in yeast via a malonyl CoA system associated with microsomal particles. An alternative or complementary system associated with mitochondria and acting

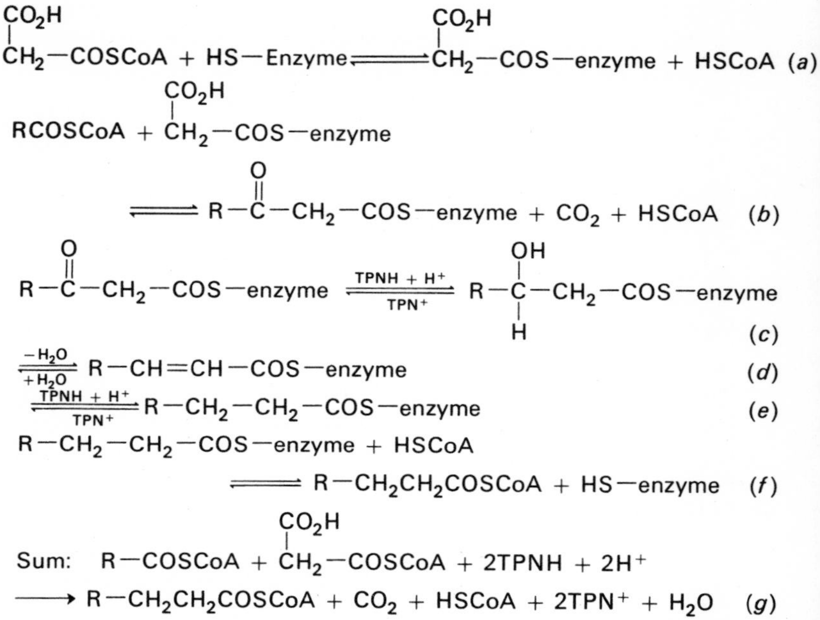

$$\begin{aligned}
&\underset{\underset{\displaystyle CH_2-COSCoA}{\overset{\displaystyle CO_2H}{|}}}{} + HS-Enzyme \rightleftharpoons \underset{\underset{\displaystyle CH_2-COS-enzyme}{\overset{\displaystyle CO_2H}{|}}}{} + HSCoA \quad (a)
\end{aligned}$$

$$RCOSCoA + \underset{\underset{\displaystyle CH_2-COS-enzyme}{\overset{\displaystyle CO_2H}{|}}}{}$$

$$\rightleftharpoons R-\overset{\displaystyle O}{\overset{||}{C}}-CH_2-COS-enzyme + CO_2 + HSCoA \quad (b)$$

$$R-\overset{\displaystyle O}{\overset{||}{C}}-CH_2-COS-enzyme \xrightarrow[TPN^+]{TPNH + H^+} R-\overset{OH}{\underset{H}{\overset{|}{\underset{|}{C}}}}-CH_2-COS-enzyme \quad (c)$$

$$\xrightarrow[+H_2O]{-H_2O} R-CH=CH-COS-enzyme \quad (d)$$

$$\xrightarrow[TPN^+]{TPNH + H^+} R-CH_2-CH_2-COS-enzyme \quad (e)$$

$$R-CH_2-CH_2-COS-enzyme + HSCoA$$

$$\rightleftharpoons R-CH_2CH_2COSCoA + HS-enzyme \quad (f)$$

$$\text{Sum:} \quad R-COSCoA + \underset{\underset{\displaystyle CH_2-COSCoA}{\overset{\displaystyle CO_2H}{|}}}{} + 2TPNH + 2H^+$$

$$\longrightarrow R-CH_2CH_2COSCoA + CO_2 + HSCoA + 2TPN^+ + H_2O \quad (g)$$

Fig. 2.9. *The reaction mechanism for the biosynthesis of saturated long-chain fatty acids by the malonyl CoA system*

(CoA = coenzyme A, TPN$^+$ = triphosphopyridine nucleotide)

by reversal of the β-oxidation pathway (discussed on p. 28) may also exist (see reviews by Wakil, 1961; Lynen, 1961). According to Lynen (1961), fatty acid synthesis is accomplished through the repetition of a cycle of six consecutive reactions (see Fig. 2.9); (a) transfer of the malonyl residue from malonyl-S-enzyme; (b) condensation of a saturated acyl CoA 'primer' (acetyl, propionyl, butyryl, etc., CoA) with the malonyl enzyme to form the β-ketoacyl enzyme, with accompanying decarboxylation driving the reaction toward synthesis; (c) reduced triphosphopyridine nucleotide (TPNH) reduction to the β-hydroxyacyl enzyme; (d) dehydration to the dehydroacyl enzyme; (e) TPNH reduction to the saturated acyl enzyme; and (f) transfer of the saturated acyl group to coenzyme A. The net result of these reactions is the elongation of the acyl CoA 'primer' by two carbon atoms, requiring 1 mole of malonyl CoA and 2 moles of TPNH. The elongated acyl CoA can then react with another malonyl enzyme. The cycle is repeated as many times as is required to give long-chain fatty acids.

Oxidation of aliphatic hydrocarbons appears to be an additional route for the synthesis of fatty acids in some micro-organisms, chiefly soil bacteria. One pathway involves oxidation of a terminal methyl group to a primary alcohol which is further oxidized to the aldehyde and finally to the acid (terminal oxidation):

$$RCH_2CH_3 \xrightarrow{O_2} RCH_2CH_2OH \xrightarrow{DPN} RCH_2CHO \xrightarrow{DPN} RCH_2CO_2H$$

Unsaturated fatty acids

The method by which the biosynthesis of unsaturated fatty acids occurs in micro-organisms has recently been elucidated by the investigations of Bloch and his associates. Two separate mechanisms exist for the synthesis of monoenoic acids. The first is an aerobic system, strictly dependent on TPNH and oxygen, which produces

$$CH_3(CH_2)_7CH_2CH_2(CH_2)_7CO_2H \xrightarrow{O_2, TPNH} \text{(oxygenated acid)}$$
stearic acid
$$\downarrow$$
$$CH_3(CH_2)_7CH=CH(CH_2)_7CO_2H$$
oleic acid

palmitoleic and oleic acids by oxidative desaturation of palmitic and stearic acids respectively, via an unidentified oxygenated intermediate: This is illustrated in Fig. 2.10.

$$CH_3(CH_2)_5CH_2CH_2(CH_2)_7CO_2H \xrightarrow{O_2, TPNH} \text{(oxygenated acid)}$$
palmitic acid
$$\downarrow$$
$$CH_3(CH_2)_5CH=CH(CH_2)_7CO_2H$$
palmitoleic acid

Fig. 2.10. Aerobic desaturation of long chain acids

The second mechanism is an anaerobic system. Experiments with *C. butyricum* in which the incorporation of carboxyl-labelled C_8 and C_{10} acids into C_{16} and C_{18} unsaturated acids was determined, led to the proposal of this alternative mechanism where the double bond in the long-chain unsaturated acid is introduced during the process of chain elongation. The key aspect of the reaction sequence leading to the long-chain unsaturated fatty acid is β,γ (rather than α,β) dehydration of one of the β-hydroxy acid intermediates formed during chain elongation. Thus the formation and isotope distribution of 9,10-hexadecenoic and 11,12-octadecenoic acids observed when *C. butyricum* is grown in the presence of $1\text{-}^{14}C$-octanoic acid can be explained by the mechanism shown in Fig. 2.11. The synthesis of a second pair of unsaturated acids in *C. butyricum*, 7,8-hexadecenoic and 9,10-octadecenoic acids, can be accounted for in an analogous manner, by β,γ-dehydration of the C_{12} β-hydroxy acid. According to this scheme, β-γ-decenoic acid should be a specific precursor of unsaturated fatty acids. Studies with labelled *cis-β-γ-*decenoic acid have shown that this compound is converted only to unsaturated fatty acids.

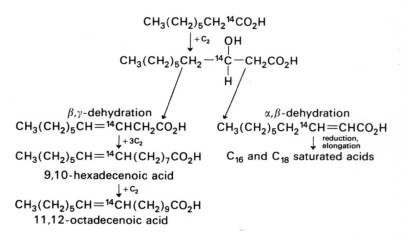

Fig. 2.11. *Mechanism for the formation of long-chain saturated and unsaturated fatty acids via β-hydroxy acid intermediate*

Branched-chain fatty acids

Synthesis of *iso* branched-chain acids in the rat adipose tissue has been shown to occur by chain elongation via the malonyl CoA system with isovaleryl CoA or isobutyryl CoA as primer.

With *iso*valeryl CoA as primer, odd-numbered branched-chain acids (chiefly C_{15} and C_{17}) are formed. With *iso*butyryl (or *iso*-caproyl) CoA the *iso* acids are even-numbered (C_{14} and C_{16}).

The anteiso-branched odd-numbered acids are synthesized from 2-methylbutyryl CoA. These are shown in Figs. 2.12 and 2.13.

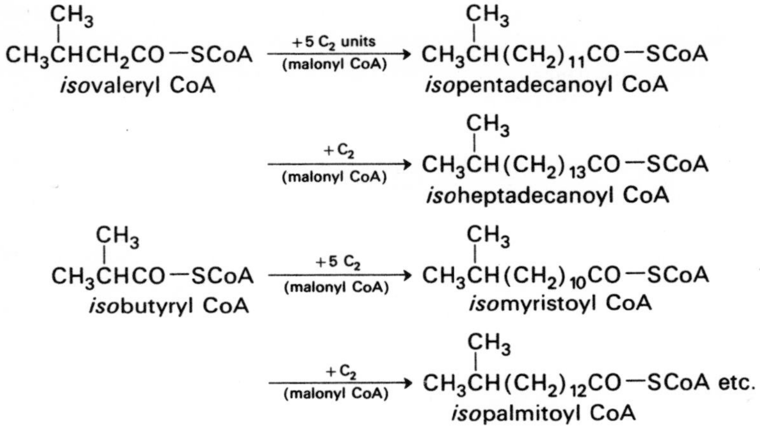

$$CH_3$$
$$|$$
$$CH_3CHCH_2CO-SCoA \xrightarrow[\text{(malonyl CoA)}]{+5\ C_2\ \text{units}} CH_3CH(CH_2)_{11}CO-SCoA$$
isovaleryl CoA   isopentadecanoyl CoA

$$CH_3$$
$$|$$
$$\xrightarrow[\text{(malonyl CoA)}]{+C_2} CH_3CH(CH_2)_{13}CO-SCoA$$
isoheptadecanoyl CoA

$$CH_3$$
$$|$$
$$CH_3CHCO-SCoA \xrightarrow[\text{(malonyl CoA)}]{+5\ C_2} CH_3CH(CH_2)_{10}CO-SCoA$$
isobutyryl CoA   isomyristoyl CoA

$$CH_3$$
$$|$$
$$\xrightarrow[\text{(malonyl CoA)}]{+C_2} CH_3CH(CH_2)_{12}CO-SCoA \text{ etc.}$$
isopalmitoyl CoA

Fig. 2.12. *The synthesis of branched-chain fatty acids*

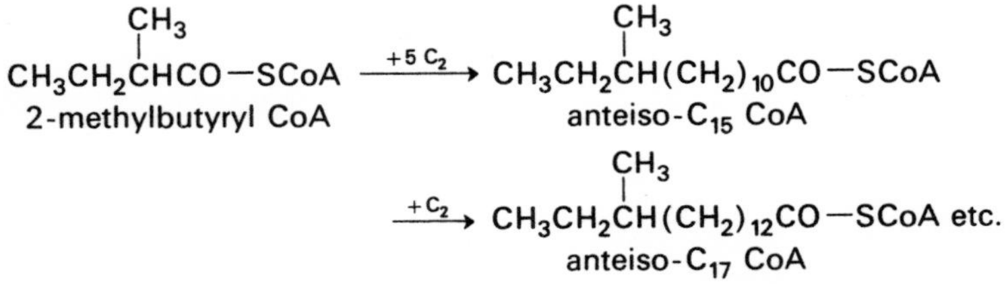

$$CH_3$$
$$|$$
$$CH_3CH_2CHCO-SCoA \xrightarrow{+5\ C_2} CH_3CH_2CH(CH_2)_{10}CO-SCoA$$
2-methylbutyryl CoA   anteiso-C_{15} CoA

$$CH_3$$
$$|$$
$$\xrightarrow{+C_2} CH_3CH_2CH(CH_2)_{12}CO-SCoA \text{ etc.}$$
anteiso-C_{17} CoA

Fig. 2.13. *The synthesis of an anteiso-branched odd-acid*

The incorporation of propionate via methyl malonyl-CoA appears to be particularly characteristic of mycobacteria. The biosynthesis of tuberculostearic acid is closely related to that of cyclopropane ring fatty acids.

Cyclopropane acids

The biosynthetic pathway of the cyclopropane acids has been worked out in some detail, as a result of the studies of several groups of investigators. Tracer techniques show that actively growing cells of *Lactobacillus arabinosus* incorporate *cis*-vaccenic acid intact into lactobacillic acid, and that the carbon atom added to form the cyclopropane ring is derived from the methyl group of methionine. The same reaction has been observed with *Escherichia coli*. The biosynthesis is illustrated in Fig. 2.14.

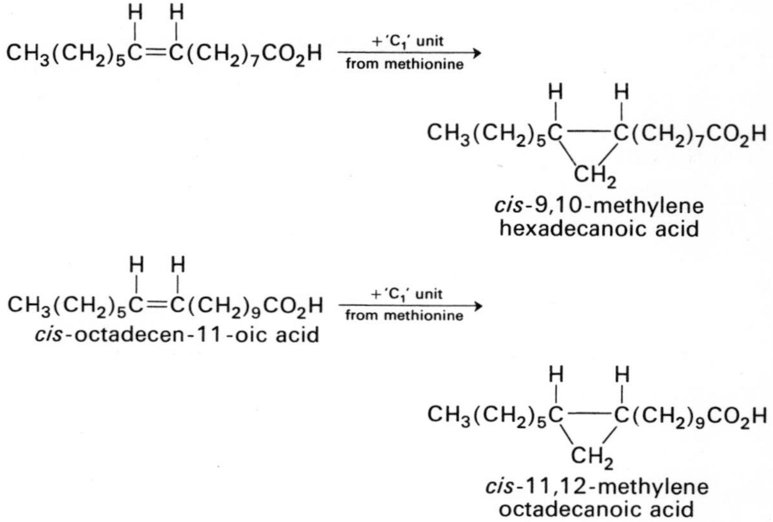

$$CH_3(CH_2)_5\overset{H}{\underset{}{C}}=\overset{H}{\underset{}{C}}(CH_2)_7CO_2H \xrightarrow[\text{from methionine}]{+ \ 'C_1' \ unit}$$

$$CH_3(CH_2)_5\overset{H}{\underset{}{C}}\underset{\underset{CH_2}{\diagdown \diagup}}{\text{———}}\overset{H}{\underset{}{C}}(CH_2)_7CO_2H$$

cis-9,10-methylene
hexadecanoic acid

$$CH_3(CH_2)_5\overset{H}{\underset{}{C}}=\overset{H}{\underset{}{C}}(CH_2)_9CO_2H \xrightarrow[\text{from methionine}]{+ \ 'C_1' \ unit}$$

cis-octadecen-11-oic acid

$$CH_3(CH_2)_5\overset{H}{\underset{}{C}}\underset{\underset{CH_2}{\diagdown \diagup}}{\text{———}}\overset{H}{\underset{}{C}}(CH_2)_9CO_2H$$

cis-11,12-methylene
octadecanoic acid

Fig. 2.14. *The biosynthesis of cyclopropane acids*

Physical Properties

Polymorphism

Except for formic and acetic acid which, in the solid state, form polymers, most *n*-carboxylic acids are hydrogen bonded through the carboxyl groups to form dimeric molecules. As the chain length increases crystallization processes become dominated by the hydrocarbon chain. This leads to the existence of polymorphic forms having different long or short X-ray spacings. The higher 'even' acids, e.g., stearic acid, can crystallize and exist in any of three crystalline forms (designated A, B, and C). The A and B forms are obtained by crystallization from a non-polar solvent, and the C-form from a polar solvent or by solidification of the fused acid. Both the A and B forms change to the C form when heated to within 10–15° of the melting point. It is the melting point of the most stable form (C) which is usually measured. The A-form has triclinic packed chains whilst both the B and C forms have orthorhombic packed chains. The 'odd' acids can crystallize in any of three polymorphic forms designated A′, B′, and C′. Crystallization from the melt for heptadecanoic acid and longer acids gives the B′-form, whilst smaller chain lengths tend to give the A′-form.

The melting points of the fatty acids vary depending upon the type of unsaturation and amount of branching as well as on the length of the chain. Thus elaidic acid has a lower melting point ($-18°C$) than stearic acid. A *cis* double bond, or a methyl side group in the fatty acid, gives a reduction of 55–60°C. This is because a single *trans* double bond does not interfere seriously with packing of neighbouring chains, whilst *cis* double bonds or methyl groups have a pronounced effect. See table 2.2.

Table 2.2. Effect of branching and unsaturation on bulk melting point of fatty acids

Common name	Structure	m.p., °C
Stearic	$n\text{-}C_{17}H_{35}CO_2H$	70
Elaidic	$C_8H_{17}CH{=}CHC_7H_{14}CO_2H$ (*trans*)	52
Oleic	$C_8H_{17}CH{=}CHC_7H_{14}CO_2H$ (*cis*)	14
Brassidic	$C_8H_{17}CH{=}CHC_{11}H_{22}CO_2H$ (*trans*)	62
Erucic	$C_8H_{17}CH{=}CHC_{11}H_{22}CO_2H$ (*cis*)	34
Linoleic	$C_5H_{11}CH{=}CHCH_2CH{=}CHC_7H_{14}CO_2H$ (*cis, cis*)	-5
Linolenic	$C_2H_5CH{=}CHCH_2CH{=}CHCH_2CH{=}CH$ $C_7H_{14}CO_2H$ (all *cis*)	-11
Tuberculostearic	$C_8H_{17}{-}\underset{\underset{CH_3}{\mid}}{CH}{-}C_8H_{16}CO_2H$	11

Monomolecular films

The lower fatty acids are soluble in water, whilst the higher members of the series are immiscible with water and spread on the surface of the water in a thin uniform layer. The films are monomolecular, i.e., one molecule thick, and are oriented so that the alkyl chain is perpendicular to the water surface, the hydrophilic carboxyl group being attracted to the water phase. These films can be compressed until the area occupied by each molecule is 20–25 Å². Further compression is resisted and leads eventually to collapse of the film. This area is independent of the length of the alkyl chain.

Whilst a given saturated fatty acid, e.g., stearic acid, at room temperature gives a condensed monolayer, the corresponding *cis* unsaturated and branched-chain acids give expanded monolayers. This behaviour parallels the bulk crystallization properties.

Analogous behaviour occurs with other monolayers. At room temperature all the *cis* unsaturated acids listed in the table give expanded films, the molecules occupying nearly the same area. Lowering the temperature to near 0°C causes elaidic acid monolayer to become more condensed, while the *cis* unsaturated films remain unexpanded. With an acid of a given chain length, as the methyl group of a branched-chain acid is moved closer to either end of the chain, the resultant film becomes less expanded.

Analysis

The analysis of the fatty acids present in lipid molecules is usually carried out by preparing the methyl esters and using the technique of gas-liquid chromatography. The size of sample required is small, ~0·5 to 30 μg. Solids are introduced either in solution or in melts. A variety of detectors is used. The fatty acid distributions in brain, mitochondria, microsomes, liver serum lipoproteins, insects, and many other lipid systems have been analysed by this method.

Ultraviolet absorption

Saturated acids containing a carboxyl group as the only chromophore absorb only in the lower range of the ultraviolet region and are not easily investigated. The introduction of one or more additional unsaturated centres increases the intensity of absorption but makes little difference to the position of absorption if the chromophores are unconjugated with each other; thus stearic, oleic, linoleic, and linolenic acids, when pure, show no useful absorption in the most easily investigated region of the ultraviolet (210–400 mμ).

When two or more chromophores are conjugated, however, there is a move in the position of maximum absorption (λ max.) into the useful region of the ultraviolet and a considerable increase in the intensity of absorption occurs. The value of λ max. depends mainly on the number of chromophores in the conjugated system and, to a lesser extent, on the actual chromophores involved and on their configuration. With fatty acids the most important chromophores are the ethylenic, acetylenic, and carboxylic groups. Conjugation is usually confined to the two former groups and seldom involves the carboxyl group. Alkali isomerization is used to move double bonds into conjugation for analytical purposes.

Infrared spectroscopy

The infrared spectrum of fatty acids gives information additional to that obtained from the ultraviolet spectrum. The most important part of the infrared range for this purpose is the fundamental region $2 \cdot 5$–15μ. Absorption bands associated with OH groups, C=O groups, CH_2, and CH_3 groups can be readily distinguished. The spectrum of the solid fatty acid often shows considerable fine structure and two different polymorphic forms will show spectral differences. The determination of the configuration of double bonds is possible with this method.

Compounds containing *cis*-double bonds differ from their *trans*-isomers in giving infrared absorption at $6 \cdot 0 \mu$ and $13 \cdot 9 \mu$. These bands tend to be obscured by other strong bands in the same region, the $6 \cdot 0 \mu$ band by absorption at about $5 \cdot 8 \mu$ due to the C=O group in acids or esters, and the $13 \cdot 9 \mu$ band by absorption arising from vibrations associated with a chain of four or more CH_2 groups. The *trans*-compounds, however, are distinctive in showing strong absorption around 10μ, the number of bands in this region and their actual position depending upon the number of bonds in conjugation.

Biological Relevance

When we discuss the biological relevance of the fatty acids we have to remember that in nature the amounts of free fatty acid which occur are quite small. Free fatty acids occur in blood, and short-chain (C_1–C_4) as well as long-chain acids (C_{12}–C_{22}) have been identified. These acids are all readily activated and oxidized by mammalian tissues. Short-chain acids are the major source of energy in ruminants.

Most of the fatty acids in nature are linked to other molecules, such as glycerol, to form glycerides, phosphoglycerides, etc. A distribution of fatty acids of varying chain length, unsaturation, and chain branching is usually observed. We shall, therefore, leave a detailed discussion of the possible relevance of the observed fatty acid distributions to each of the appropriate chapters dealing with the combined lipid molecules. Here we shall only make a few general observations: (a) The proportion of oleic and linoleic acid in plant seeds can be varied considerably merely by changing the condition of growth. (b) The castor bean is unusual in having hydroxy acid in its storage fat whilst other seeds are unusual in having only a single fatty acid in their lipid. (c) Some rough correlations have been observed between temperature and fatty acid distribution; thus fish which live in a cold environment have higher unsaturated acids in their lipids than normal. Furthermore, the oil of a plant grown in a hot climate has more saturated fatty acids present than a plant grown in a cold climate. We shall discuss this further in chapters 3 and 4.

Despite the importance of these unsaturated fatty acids they are not essential for life. The lipids of *Clostridium welchii* contain no unsaturation and lactobacilli grown on a biotin-free media can meet their fatty acid requirement from a cyclopropane or lactobacillic acid. It has been suggested that the presence of branched-chain fatty acids in mycobacteria is to help the bacteria to resist the enzymatic response of host tissues. It has also been suggested that the fatty acid composition of a particular micro-organism might be a useful tool for the classification of the organism. However, the fatty acid composition of bacterial lipids can change with the physiological age of the culture.

If we pose our question differently and ask what we know about the biological relevance of individual acids, there are a few pointers to specific rather than more general functions. It has been known for some time that certain fatty acids, such as linoleic, linolenic, and arachidonic acids are essential for the living animal. Some animal species cannot exist without a supply of linoleic acid in the diet. The exact function of the essential fatty acids is not yet known. Recently, however, it has been established that, amongst other functions, the essential fatty acids are precursors of molecules called prostaglandins. Prostaglandins are present in animal tissues, particularly in the vesicular glands of sheep and the seminal fluid of sheep and man, and have important physiological properties.

Thus arachidonic acid has been shown to convert by an enzyme system to prostaglandins. The structure of prostaglandin PGE_2 is shown, Fig. 2.15. Homo-γ-linolenic acid has also been converted to prostaglandin E in a similar manner.

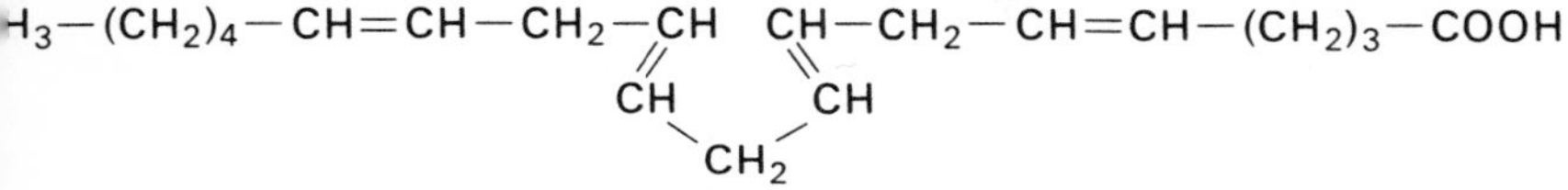

Arachidonic acid

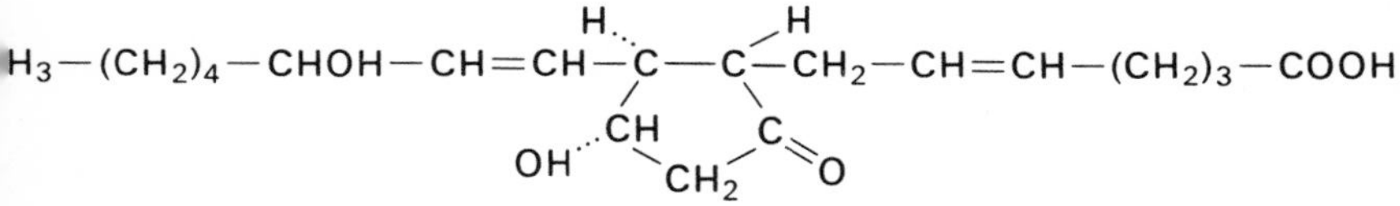

Prostaglandin E_2

Fig. 2.15. *The structures of arachidonic acid and prostaglandin E_2*

Linoleic acid (octadeca-9,12-dienoic acid) has been found in almost every higher protist, plant, and animal so far examined. It has been considered to have particular relevance for photosynthetic activity, although this correlation is not certain (see chapter 6). The blue-green algae *Anacystis* can carry out photosynthesis without containing this acid. The more highly evolved protists, including *Anabaena*, possess the ability to synthesize α-linolenic acid and utilize it to the benefit of the photosynthetic systems and, in this way, evolve towards total dependence on this acid. The biosynthesis of fatty acids in protists, particularly oleic acid and either or both of the positional isomers of linolenic acid from linoleic acid, has been examined to suggest phylogenetic relationships and throw light on ancestral evolutionary pathways.

Further Reading

General

F. D. Gunstone, *An Introduction to the Chemistry of Fats and Fatty Acids*, Wiley, 1958.

J. Asselineau, *Les Lipides Bacteriens*. Hermann, Paris, 1962.

R. Shaw, *Advances in Lipid Research*, **4**, 107. Academic Press, 1966.
K. S. Markley, *Fatty Acids*, Part 3. Interscience Publishers, 1963.

Biosynthesis of fatty acids

F. Lynen, *Federation Proceedings*, **20**, 941, 1961.
S. J. Wakil, *Ann. Rev. Biochem.*, **31**, 369, 1962.
R. Vagelos, *Ann. Rev. Biochem.*, **33**, 139, 1964.
M. Kates, *Advances in Lipid Research*, **2**, p. 1. Academic Press, 1964.

Physical properties

G. A. J. Pitt and R. A. Morton, *Progress in the Chemistry of Fats and Other Lipids*. Pergamon Press, 1957.
S. Abrahamsson, *Arkiv. Kemi*, **14**, 65, 1959.
D. Chapman, *The Structure of Lipids*, p. 243, Methuen, London, 1965.
G. L. Gaines, *Insoluble monolayers at liquid-gas interfaces*. Interscience, 1966.

Biological properties

S. Bergström *et al.*, *Biochim. Biophys. Acta*, **90**, 207, 1964.
D. A. van Dorp *et al.*, *Biochim. Biophys. Acta*, **90**, 204, 1964.
G. Blix, ed., *Polyunsaturated fatty acids as Nutrients*. Symposia of the Swedish Nutritional Foundation IV, Almqvist & Wiksells, 1966.
S. Bergstrom, *Science*, **157**, 382, 1967.

3. Neutral Lipids

The most abundant fatty acid derivatives in plant and animal tissues are the simple lipids which include glycerides and cholesterol esters. Glyceryl ethers are also found to occur in small amounts. These lipids are uncharged and therefore are often called neutral lipids.

A. Glycerides

Structure and occurrence

The glycerides are all derived from esterification of glycerol. A numbering system is used to indicate that the primary carbinol groups are not interchangeable. With glycerol if the secondary

$$
\begin{array}{ll}
CH_2OH & (1) \\
\mid & \\
HOCH & (2) \\
\mid & \\
CH_2OH & (3)
\end{array}
$$

Glycerol (*sn*-numbering to right)

hydroxyl group is shown to the left of C-2 in a Fischer projection, the carbon atom above C-2 is called C-1, the one below C-3; the use of this 'stereospecific' numbering is indicated by the prefix '*sn*' before the stem-name of the compound. With such a terminology for distinguishing the two primary carbinol groups of free glycerol, a logical extension has been to describe the stereochemistry of derivatives by indicating the carbon atoms that are substituted (see appendix). The various glyceride types are shown in Fig. 3.1.

The triglycerides constitute well over 98 per cent of the lipids of the adipose tissue of the mammal, 30 per cent of the plasma and liver lipids, but less than 10 per cent of the red blood cell lipids.

The triglycerides are present in largest amounts but diglycerides and monoglycerides have been isolated from certain tissues. It can be seen that two isomeric diglyceride and monoglyceride types may

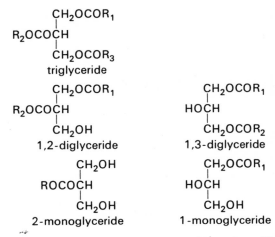

Fig. 3.1. *The structures of various glyceride types. (Recently the terms triacylglycerol and diacylglycerol have been suggested for the more traditional terms triglycerides and diglycerides)*

occur. Even with the triglycerides a large number of possibilities can occur, dependent upon the position of the fatty acids. The various possibilities are shown where only two fatty acids, stearic and oleic acid, are considered, Fig. 3.2. The nomenclature used to designate the positions of the groups is also given. (At one time a nomenclature using the letters α and β was used. As polymorphism was also designated in this way, see page 56, this led to confusion. The present nomenclature is preferred.)

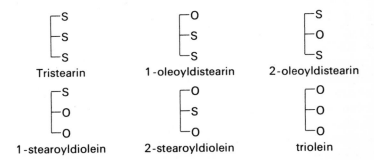

Fig. 3.2. *The various triglyceride structures possible using two different fatty acids*

The observed distribution of the fatty acids in natural triglycerides is not a random distribution. Many theories have been put forward to explain this. One theory suggests that any particular acid is as widely distributed as possible over the different triglycerides. Other theories include the concept that the acids are distributed according to a random pattern, except that the content of the fully saturated triglyceride is limited by the amount which can remain fluid *in vivo*.

The fatty acids present in the naturally occurring glycerides vary considerably depending upon the type of animal or plant in which they occur. A few generalizations have been made.

(a) The depot fats of the higher land animals consist mainly of palmitic acid (25–30 per cent) and oleic acid frequently accompanied by high proportions of stearic acid. The total content of C_{18} acids is generally about 70 per cent.

(b) Glycerides of aquatic origin are characterized by the wide range of acids present. There is a low content of saturated acids and high unsaturation of the C_{20} and C_{22} acids.

(c) Palmitic and oleic acids are always major components of milk fats and there are usually saturated short-chain acids present.

(d) Seed glycerides contain palmitic, oleic, linoleic, and/or linolenic acid. Within a botanical family the fatty acid content is similar. Sometimes a major component acid is characteristic of a whole plant family or only a few species.

The separation of pure individual glycerides from complex natural mixtures is a matter of considerable difficulty, and relatively few have been isolated in the pure state. For the study of the physical properties of these compounds and for identification of natural products when isolated, it is necessary to devise methods of synthesis of the various types.

Chemical Synthesis of Glycerides

It is now possible to prepare with relative ease all types of glycerides. Apart from the monacid triglycerides, which are readily obtained by direct esterification of glycerol, the preparation of other types involves further acylation of mono- and di-glycerides, which are, therefore, key substances in glyceride chemistry. In general, the reactions involved in their preparation are standard methods of protection, acylation and interchange, but one unusual feature is the possibility of acyl migration. This appears to be of the following two types:

(a) Migration of the 2-acyl group to the 1 position:

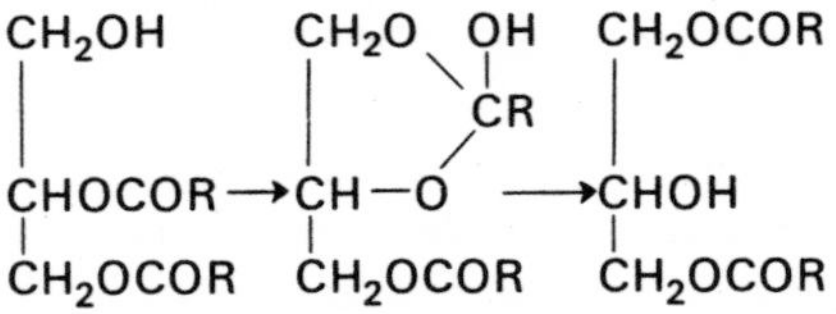

$$
\begin{array}{ccc}
CH_2OH & CH_2OOH & CH_2OCOR \\
| & |\backslash| & | \\
& CR & \\
CHOCOR \rightarrow CH-O & \longrightarrow CHOH \\
| & | & | \\
CH_2OCOR & CH_2OCOR & CH_2OCOR
\end{array}
$$

This migration is rapid in the presence of acid, and it is also brought about by alkali or heat. For monoglycerides an equilibrium is set up favouring 1-monoglyceride, which exists in the mixture to the extent of 90–92 per cent.

(b) The second type of migration occurs in the opposite direction, i.e., from the 1 to the 2 position, during the interchange between iodides and silver salts of fatty acids. No migration occurs when the above reaction is carried out with $1:2$-diacyl glycerol iodide.

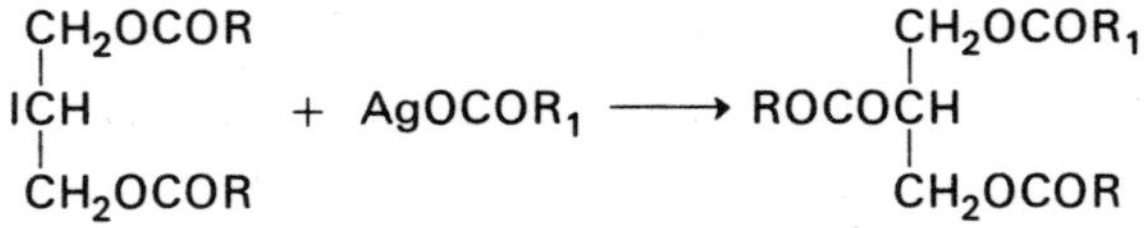

$$
\begin{array}{ccccc}
CH_2OCOR & & & & CH_2OCOR_1 \\
| & & & & | \\
ICH & + & AgOCOR_1 & \longrightarrow & ROCOCH \\
| & & & & | \\
CH_2OCOR & & & & CH_2OCOR
\end{array}
$$

The above migration probably proceeds as follows:

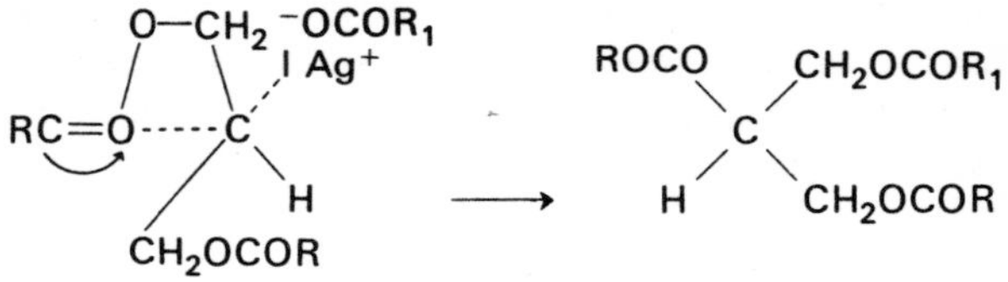

(a) *Monoglycerides.* By far the best method of preparation, and the one most widely used, is that which uses $1:2$-isopropylidine glycerol as a starting material. This is readily prepared in good yield, from glycerol and acetone, and its structure is known. The acyl group is introduced by means of the acid chloride, the free acid or the

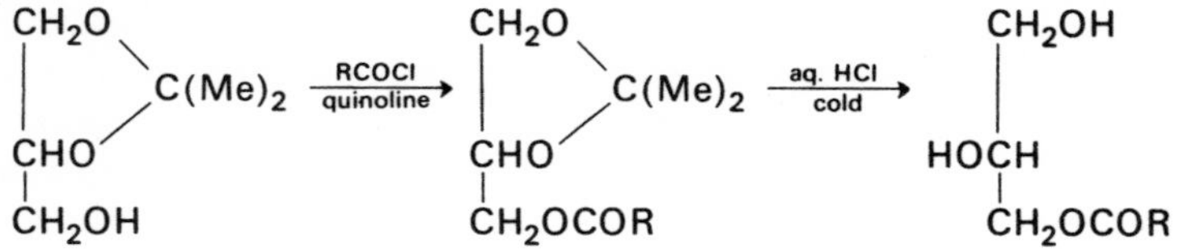

$$\underset{\underset{CH_2OH}{|}}{\overset{\overset{CH_2O}{|}}{CHO}}C(Me)_2 \xrightarrow[\text{quinoline}]{RCOCl} \underset{\underset{CH_2OCOR}{|}}{\overset{\overset{CH_2O}{|}}{CHO}}C(Me)_2 \xrightarrow[\text{cold}]{\text{aq. HCl}} \underset{\underset{CH_2OCOR}{|}}{\overset{\overset{CH_2OH}{|}}{HOCH}}$$

Fig. 3.3. Synthesis of 1-monoglycerides

methyl ester. The reaction is shown. Acetone is split off the resulting product by the action of hydrochloric acid in the cold to yield the 1-monoglyceride. The acylation can be carried out in inert solvents, such as benzene or chloroform, in the presence of quinoline or pyridine, or the intermediate may be made by passing dry hydrogen chloride into a solution of the fatty acid in isopropylidine glycerol. Excellent yields are obtained by all methods, Fig. 3.3.

High yields are also obtained in the final stage for derivatives of saturated acids higher than C_{12}, but for derivatives of shorter chain acids and unsaturated acids, the resulting monoglycerides are more soluble in the aqueous hydrolysing medium, and there is a tendency to hydrolyse off the fatty acid as well as the acetone. The use of 10 per cent aqueous acetic acid at 60°C enables the acetone group only to be removed.

A similar method uses 1:2-benzylidine glycerol as the starting material instead of isopropylidine glycerol. This is acylated with the appropriate acid chlorides in pyridine, and the resulting intermediates, which are easily purified by crystallization, are hydrolysed by cold aqueous hydrochloric acid to give very high yields of 1-monoglycerides.

Another starting material is glycerol 1-iodohydrin. This is acylated in good yield, in the presence of pyridine or quinoline, to give an intermediate which is easily purified by crystallization. On warming this intermediate with aqueous alcoholic silver nitrite, the iodine atom is replaced by hydroxyl. See Fig. 3.4.

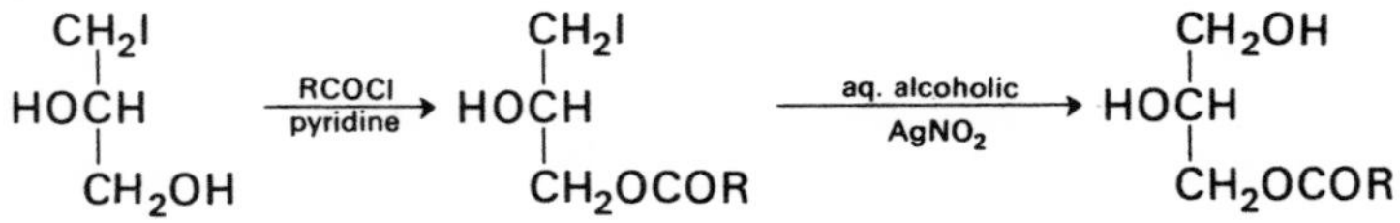

$$\underset{\underset{CH_2OH}{|}}{\overset{\overset{CH_2I}{|}}{HOCH}} \xrightarrow[\text{pyridine}]{RCOCl} \underset{\underset{CH_2OCOR}{|}}{\overset{\overset{CH_2I}{|}}{HOCH}} \xrightarrow[\text{AgNO}_2]{\text{aq. alcoholic}} \underset{\underset{CH_2OCOR}{|}}{\overset{\overset{CH_2OH}{|}}{HOCH}}$$

Fig. 3.4. Synthesis of 1-monoglycerides from glycerol 1-iodohydrin

(b) *1:3-Diglycerides.* All the earlier methods are unsatisfactory in one respect or another, and the first reliable method starts by acylating glycerol 1-iodohydrin with 2 moles of acid chloride in the presence of quinoline (pyridine serves equally well). The readily purified, crystalline product is refluxed with aqueous alcoholic silver nitrite.

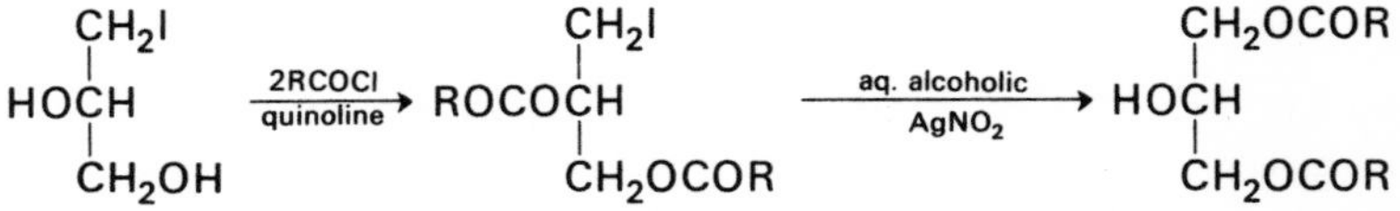
CH2I
HOCH
CH2OH
2RCOCl
quinoline
CH2I
ROCOCH
CH2OCOR
aq. alcoholic
AgNO2
CH2OCOR
HOCH
CH2OCOR

In the final stage, hydrolysis of the iodide and acyl migration occurs.

The method is readily adapted to the preparation of diacid 1:3-diglycerides. Acylation with a mole of acid chloride, yields the 3-acyl 1-iodo compound which can be purified by crystallization and further acylated with a different acid chloride. Treatment with silver nitrite then yields a mixed 1:3-diglyceride, Fig. 3.5.

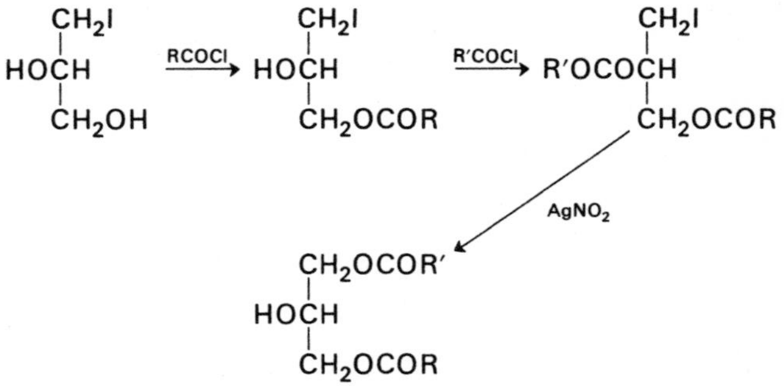
CH2I
HOCH
CH2OH
RCOCl
CH2I
HOCH
CH2OCOR
R′COCl
CH2I
R′OCOCH
CH2OCOR
AgNO2
CH2OCOR′
HOCH
CH2OCOR

Fig. 3.5. *The synthesis of a diacid 1:3-diglyceride*

Another excellent method of preparation, particularly for diglycerides of the higher fatty acids, i.e., C_{14} upwards, makes use of the acylation of the 1-monotrityl ether of glycerol. This is easily prepared and the trityl groups removed by treatment with a solution of dry hydrogen chloride gas in ether or petrol ether. The only objection to this synthesis is that, for the more soluble diglycerides, the removal of the triphenylhalide by-products by crystallization brings about a loss in yield.

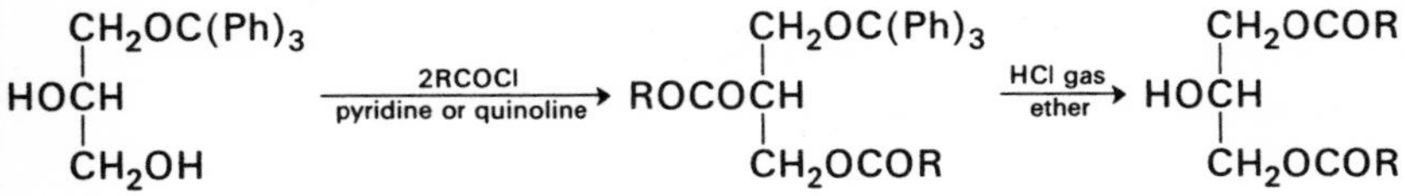

$$\begin{array}{c} CH_2OC(Ph)_3 \\ | \\ HOCH \\ | \\ CH_2OH \end{array} \xrightarrow[\text{pyridine or quinoline}]{\text{2RCOCl}} \begin{array}{c} CH_2OC(Ph)_3 \\ | \\ ROCOCH \\ | \\ CH_2OCOR \end{array} \xrightarrow[\text{ether}]{\text{HCl gas}} \begin{array}{c} CH_2OCOR \\ | \\ HOCH \\ | \\ CH_2OCOR \end{array}$$

(c) *1:2-Diglycerides*. The preparation of these compounds is a matter of some difficulty because of the ready migration of the 2-acyl group, and consequently the usual acid reagents for removing protecting groups cannot be used. The only satisfactory methods of preparation involve (i) the protection of one primary hydroxyl group of glycerol; (ii) complete acylation; (iii) removal of the protecting group by catalytic hydrogenolysis. The following scheme gives a high yield at each stage, Fig. 3.6.

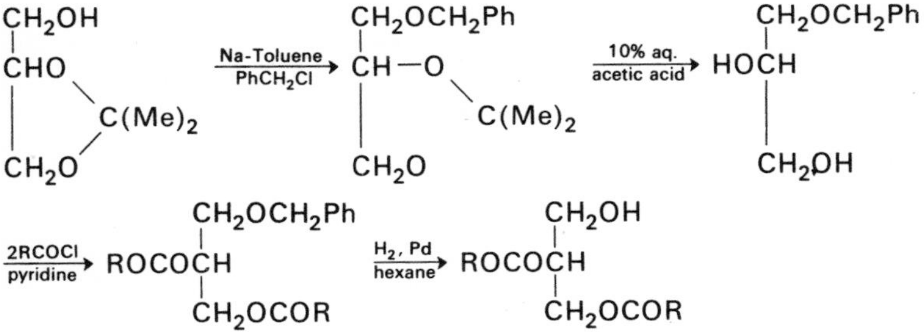

Fig. 3.6. *Synthesis of a 1:2-diglyceride*

All the above methods are readily adapted to the preparation of diacid 1:2-diglycerides. Recently the preparation of unsaturated 1:2-diglycerides has also been described.

(d) *Diacid diglycerides (mixed diglycerides)*. All the methods starting from a 1-protected glycerol (including monoglycerides and glycerol 1-iodohydrin) can be used for the preparation of mixed diglycerides by acylating in stages with different acyl chlorides or acid. 1-Protected glycerol acylates preferentially in the 3 position, and conditions should be such as to avoid acylation in the 2 position as well. A useful method is shown in Fig. 3.7.

The simple method for preparing 1,2-diglycerides with a wide range of fatty acid compositions is to carry out an incomplete acylization of two monoglycerides, followed by chromatographic

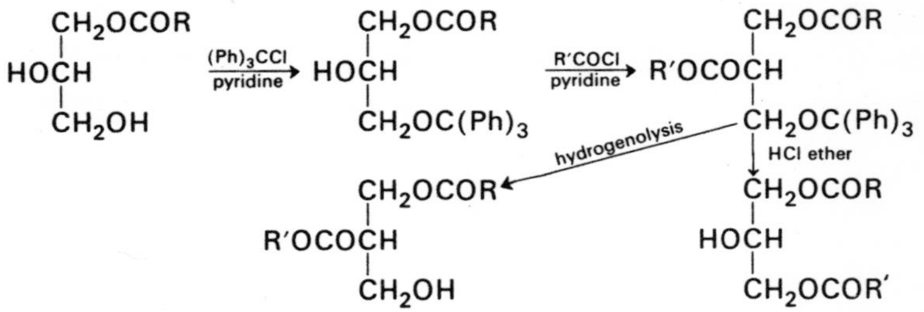

Fig. 3.7. *Synthesis of mixed acid diglycerides*

separation. The acylation is carried out by adding an equimolar amount of fatty acid glyceride to limit the time of reaction.

(e) *Triglycerides.* The monoacid or simple triglycerides are readily prepared by heating a small excess of the theoretical amount of fatty acid with glycerol, at 140–150°C for a few hours in the presence of 1–2 per cent of *p*-toluenesulphonic acid. Alternatively, and preferably, if the acids are unsaturated, glycerol is acylated in the presence of excess of pyridine or quinoline, with three moles of acid chloride.

The *unsymmetrical* diacid triglycerides are prepared by acylating 1-monoglycerides with two moles of acid chloride in the standard manner. It is possible to prepare these compounds by the acylation of 1:2-diglycerides, or by the interaction of a silver salt of a fatty acid and 1:3-diacyl-2-glycerol iodohydrin. These methods, however, obviously cannot compete in simplicity with the former method.

The *symmetrical* diacid triglycerides can be made by the acylation of 1:3-diglycerides in the standard manner. It is advisable to use a moderate excess of acid chloride, and when using unsaturated acid chlorides, a large excess and an elevated temperature may be required. Excess of acid in the final product is easily removed by crystallization from alcohol in which triglycerides are only slightly soluble.

(f) *Optically active glycerides.* Optically active monoglycerides are prepared by acylation of the isopropylidene glycerol with a fatty acid chloride followed by removal of the isopropylidene group by the action of hydrochloric acid in the cold. The analytical values obtained on these monoglycerides show them to be the 1-isomer.

For the synthesis of optically active diglycerides, the D- or L-*iso*propylidene glycerol is used to prepare 1-benzyl glycerol ether.

Saturated, monoacid diglycerides are obtained by acylation with fatty acid chloride and removal of the benzyl group by hydrogenolysis. The last step limits this method to the preparation of saturated diglycerides.

Diacid diglycerides have also been synthesized. The fatty acids are introduced in a four-step process starting with optically active 1-benzyl glycerol ether. Acylation is carried out with a fatty acid chloride. The successive steps are: (i) tritylation of the 1-benzyl glycerol ether, (ii) acylation of the remaining free hydroxyl group, which is in the 2-position, (iii) removal of the trityl group with a simultaneous shift of the fatty acid from the 2- to the 1-position by hydrogen chloride in petroleum ether, and (iv) introduction of the second fatty acid into the 2-position.

The partial glycerides pose a special problem because of the ease with which they isomerize. The section on synthesis has pointed out the problems which exist in the preparation of glycerides as a result of this instability.

Analysis

Glycerides containing an unsaturated fatty acid have to be protected from oxidation by excluding such agents as metals, oxygen, heat, and light. They are best stored under nitrogen in tightly sealed containers in the cold. Stability is further assured by the addition, at a level of about 50 parts per million, of antioxidants such as butylated hydroxyanisole, butylated hydroxytoluene, nordihydroguaiaretic acid, and hydroquinone or tocopherol. Hydroquinone has the advantage that it can be removed from the glycerides by water-washing.

There is little difficulty in extracting triglycerides from tissues such as adipose tissue or oil seeds. In general triglycerides are not bound into lipoprotein or lipocarbohydrate complexes. The wet tissue can be extracted with successive acetone washes.

Stability and separation

The storage and stability of glycerides are of some importance. At the present time it is possible to resolve mixtures of mono-, di-, and triglycerides and to separate the two diglyceride isomers. It is also

possible to separate 1-monoglycerides from 2-monoglycerides by
thin-layer chromatography using a special adsorbent (hydroxyl
apatite). Only very simple glyceride mixtures can be fractionated on
the basis of their fatty acid composition. The introduction of one
double bond into one of the fatty acids of a glyceride alters its
separation characteristics, in many of the methods.

Low-temperature solvent crystallization is among the early
methods used for the separation and fractionation of glycerides.
The method is tedious and the yields may be poor. However, there
are many areas of glyceride chemistry where it is an invaluable tool.
The manipulations involved are least likely to cause alteration of
the lipids. Much of the early work on the structure of glycerides in
natural fats relied on this method.

Chromatographic techniques

The technique of gas–liquid chromatography has been applied to
the analysis of triglycerides. Simple mixtures of monoacid triglycerides can be separated on suitable columns; however, natural
triglycerides are made up of such a wide variety of triglycerides that
these are only partially resolved.

Some success has been obtained in applying gas–liquid chromatography to the measurement of partial glycerides. This is best accomplished with a derivative that increases the volatility of the partial
glyceride, e.g., the acetylated products of mono- and diglycerides.
Another method is to convert monoglycerides to their allyl esters.
A method has been developed for the simultaneous determination
of glycerol content and fatty acid composition. In this, glycerides
are treated with lithium aluminium hydride, the resulting lithium
aluminium alcoholates are acetylated, and these are analysed by
gas–liquid chromatography. The method does not yield any information about the structure of the glycerides, but it is useful for determining glycerol content and glycerol-to-fatty-acid ratios.

Column chromatography is the method most widely used for
the fractionation of lipids. Initially many of the adsorbents that
were taken from non-lipid fields were found to be of little value.
For example, alumina cannot be used because it causes isomerization of double bonds, hydrolysis of ester linkages, and isomerization
of partial glycerides. With the introduction of silicic acid columns,
the separation of various lipid classes was readily accomplished.

This adsorbent is the one most widely used, although subsequently others have been introduced that have advantages for certain systems.

Even though thin-layer chromatography is among the more recent methods to be introduced into the field of lipid chemistry, it has already shown itself to be of great value. Although the technique itself has been known for a number of years, and has found extensive application in the field of terpenes, it was not until 1956, through the work of Stahl, that its use in the lipid field was established.

Mono-, di-, and triglycerides are readily separated by thin-layer chromatography. A ready separation of 1,2- from 1,3-diglycerides can also be obtained. 1-Monoglycerides can be separated from 2-monoglycerides but care has to be taken to avoid isomerization, either by using rapid development, or by working at low temperatures ($\sim 10°C$). Using thin-layer chromatography, the mixtures of triglycerides present in natural oils and fats have been successfully separated.

The mono-, di-, and triglycerides are separated by chromatography over silica. The triglycerides can be separated according to their degree of unsaturation by means of chromatography over silica impregnated with silver nitrate. Triglycerides having the same number of double bonds occur together. The fatty acid composition at the 2-position is determined by micro-lipase splitting. If the oil is hydrogenated the triglyceride composition of this material can be determined using gas–liquid chromatography which separates the glycerides according to molecular weight.

Lipase activity

The use of lipases affords a mild, selective means of degradation of triglycerides and has proved useful in analysis for assigning the position of attachment of constituent fatty acids. The lipases may be classified as hydrolases, catalysing the hydrolytic cleavage of the fatty acids from the triglycerides. This type of attack may be illustrated by the following equation:

$$RCO_2R_1 + HOH \rightleftharpoons RCO_2H + R_1OH$$

which shows the hydrolytic as well as the synthetic action of these enzymes. If the ester is of low molecular weight and a simple type, i.e., ethyl butyrate, then this is an example of an esterase activity. If the ester is a glyceryl derivative and contains long-chain fatty acids, then these enzymes are called the lipases.

Lipases from various sources have varying positional specificity. Whereas pancreatic lipase has specificity for 1,3-positions of the triglyceride molecule, some bacterial and plant lipases have either specificity for 2-position or no specificity at all.

Analysis of the triglyceride fatty acids is based upon the assumption that the pancreatic lipase (generally used in this type of study) possesses no fatty acid specificity. There is ample evidence that the enzyme possesses specificity for fatty acids, especially short chain fatty acids when various glycerides are present in the substrate. This specificity is called intermolecular specificity and is not to be confused with intramolecular specificity which is absent in pancreatic lipase. The problem of migration of acyl groups from 2-position to 1-position of triglyceride is generally avoided by using very short incubation periods of the order of 5 minutes. Caution is needed in interpreting the results obtained in pancreatic lipolysis technique.

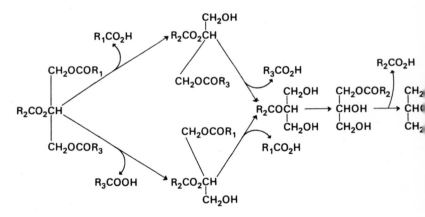

Fig. 3.8. *Specificity of pancreatic lipase*

The action of lipases gives rise to a series of reactions from triglycerides to diglycerides to monoglycerides. Ultimately, if calcium ion is present, glycerol and fatty acid are formed, Fig. 3.8.

Following a meal rich in triglycerides, during digestion of the triglycerides by pancreatic lipase, 2-monoglycerides are formed. For complete hydrolysis a shift to the 1-position seems to be necessary. Lipolysis is activated by bile salts. These activators aid in the emulsification of fats, but also displace the pH optimum from pH 8·0 to 6·0, and increase lipolysis to a degree which could not be explained simply by the enlargement of interface area.

The extent of hydrolysis: The extent to which hydrolysis actually progresses is not easy to establish from observations on the intestinal contents of animals during fat absorption. The formation of breakdown products goes on concurrently with their adsorption, and the contents of the intestinal lumen are the result of two competing processes, i.e., lipolysis and resorption.

Biosynthesis of Triglycerides

The pathway of fatty acid esterification to triglycerides had been worked out with homogenates of liver, but later was found to proceed in a similiar way in all other tissues examined. The incorporation of

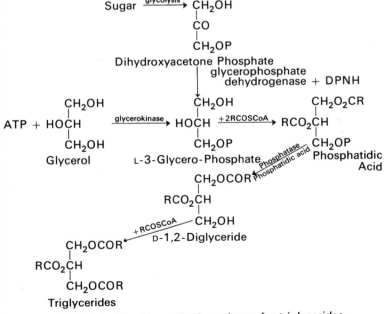

Fig. 3.9. The biosynthetic pathway for triglycerides

[14]C labelled palmitic acid into triglycerides by rat-liver homogenates was found to depend on the presence of ATP. This showed that triglyceride synthesis is not brought about by the reversal of its degradation by lipolytic enzymes. It pointed to the necessity for an ATP-dependent activation of the fatty acid to form fatty acyl CoA. Such activation has previously been shown to be necessary for esterification. The acceptor for the fatty acid moiety is not free glycerol but L-3-glycerophosphate, producing phosphatidic acid. Glycerol can serve as precursor only when converted to 3-glycerophosphate by a glycerokinase, present in liver, again requiring ATP. 3-Glycerophosphate can also be formed by the reduction of dihydroxy-acetone-phosphate, an intermediate of the glycolytic breakdown of sugars. The pathway is shown in Fig. 3.9.

3-Glycerophosphate is essential for the formation of triglycerides by liver microsomes and mitochondria.

Triglyceride synthesis is in line with the synthesis of phospholipids, which proceeds by removal of the phosphate from phosphatidic acid, with the formation of a 1,2-diglyceride. The diglyceride can be converted into phospholipid by cytidinediphosphatecholine or ethanolamine, or into neutral triglycerides by the addition of one more fatty acid derived from fatty acylcoenzyme A. Another biosynthetic pathway for triglycerides involves monoglycerides and also requires ATP.

Physical Properties

Because of the considerable technological importance of the glyceride molecules, a great deal of study has been made of their physical properties. Here we shall merely comment on some of the main points of these properties.

Polymorphism

Like the fatty acids the glycerides can exist in a variety of different crystal forms. Some glycerides can exist in two, three, and even five, different forms. The glycerides show the phenomena of multiple melting points associated with transitions from one form to another. The study of polymorphism has led to many controversies and it is only recently that these have been resolved. However, the nomenclature used for designating different polymorphic forms is confusing due to the fact that the same symbols were used with different

Table 3.1. X-ray and melting data of the three polymorphic forms of a series of triglycerides

Glyceride	Melting points °C			X-ray long spacings			X-ray short spacings		
	α_L	β'_L	β_L	α_L	β'_L	β_L	α_L	β'_L	β_L
Tristearin	54	64	73·1	50·6	47·2	45·0	4·2 3·8s 4·22s	—	3·7m 3·9m 4·6s 5·3m
Tripalmitin	44·7	56·6	66·4	45·6	42·6	40·6	4·2 3·8s 4·22s	—	3·7m 3·9m 4·6s 5·3m
Trimyristin	33	46·5	57·0	41·2	37·6	35·8	4·2 3·8s 4·22s	—	3·7m 3·9m 4·6s 5·3m
Trilaurin	15	35·0	46·4	35·6	32·9	31·2	4·2 3·78s 4·18vs	—	3·7m 3·9m 4·6s 5·3m

association. The polymorphism of glycerides has been studied by a whole range of physical techniques. A full discussion is given in the review by Chapman, e.g., X-ray, infrared and n.m.r. spectroscopy, dilatometry, dielectric, and melting studies are reported.

The X-ray and melting data for some triglycerides are shown in Table 3.1. In order to give an impression of the polymorphic behaviour of a simple triglyceride, we shall discuss the behaviour of a typical triglyceride, e.g., tristearin. If we start with the melted glyceride then

(a) On being cooled from the melt to below room temperature it crystallizes in the α_L-form. A single X-ray short spacing at about 4·1 Å is observed (see page 9 for discussion of short spacings). There is a fair degree of freedom of the chains to move in this form.

(b) If this α_L-form is heated to its melting point (54°C) a rapid transformation occurs to the most stable β_L-form. This gives a strong 4·6 Å spacing. Further heating causes the β_L-form to melt at 73°C.

(c) If, however, the liquid melt is cooled only to a temperature a few degrees *above* the α_L-melting point and is held at this temperature, an intermediate β'_L-form occurs; this is recognized by the presence of X-ray short spacings at 3·8 and 4·2 Å.

(d) On heating this form, a transition occurs to the stable β_L-form and further heating causes the β_L-form to melt at 73°C.

These phase transitions are clearly revealed (Fig. 3.10) using thermal analysis methods for a number of simple triglycerides.

All the various triglycerides containing different chain lengths and different amounts of unsaturation exhibit polymorphism. The mono- and diglycerides also exhibit polymorphic behaviour. The basis of this behaviour lies mainly in the various modes of hydrocarbon chain packing which can occur in the crystalline condition, and the different angles of tilt which the chains can have.

Polymorphism is of technological relevance because the rheological properties of the forms differ. Cocoa butter exhibits marked polymorphism and this is of considerable importance in chocolate manufacture. The first correct identification of the major glyceride of cocoa butter, showing that the oleic acid was in the 2-position, was made possible because the closely related 1-oleo disaturated and 2-oleo disaturated triglycerides crystallize in two different polymorphic forms. These different crystalline forms give rise to markedly different infrared spectra. This made identification of the appropriate isomer relatively simple.

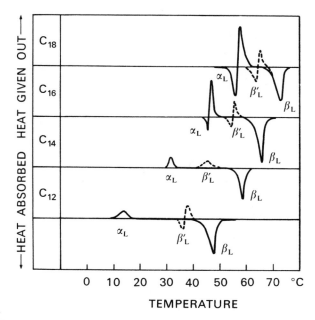

Fig. 3.10. Differential heating curves of a series of triglycerides

Properties in water

Triglycerides and diglycerides do not interact with water in bulk. Their solubilities are extremely low; an excess is present as an oil. Monoglycerides are polar lipids, either the 1- or 2-isomer behaving as non-ionic analogues of phospholipids, i.e., as swelling amphipaths. They are insoluble in water, yet disperse in hydrated aggregates. Such dispersion can occur only at or above the transition temperature of a given monoglyceride; for a straight-chain saturated monoglyceride, this is 17 to 27°C below the anhydrous melting point. Monoglycerides have properties which are somewhat similar to the diacyl lecithins in forming various types of liquid crystalline phases in water. Lawrence has suggested that monoglycerides and phospholipids are members of a large class of compounds occurring in nature which always remain associated with water, and that it is helpful to show that water is soluble in them even if they are insoluble in water. At 37° monoglycerides of low melting point have remarkably high micellar solubilities in bile salt solutions.

Monomolecular films

When the total number of carbon atoms present in triglycerides is more than 20, fully saturated triglycerides form stable monolayers. At room temperature expanded films are observed with short chains, whilst with tripalmitin and longer-chain triglycerides, condensed monolayers are obtained.

The condensed monolayer gives a molecular area near to 60 $Å^2$ corresponding to the three chains present in the molecule.

B. Glyceryl Ethers

Structure and Occurrence

In contrast to the lipid ester and amide linkages normally encountered in nature, the occurrence of a lipid ether grouping is limited. The structure of a glyceryl ether is shown in chapter 1. By their possible close relationship to the plasmalogens, see chapter 4, the glyceryl ethers may well be precursors or possible metabolic products of these phosphorylated glyceryl ethers.

The naturally occurring ethers are α-glyceryl ethers; a centre of asymmetry is present and hence D and L forms are possible. The synthesis of D-α- and L-α-selachyl alcohol was of considerable value in establishing the correct configuration.

Chemical Synthesis

This synthesis is accomplished in the following manner:

α-(p-toluene sulphonyl)-acetone glycerol
         +
    Na salt of oleyl alcohol
              └────→ Condensation product ────→ α-oleyl glyceryl ether
                                                    (selachyl alcohol)

Depending on the use of either the D or L acetone derivative as starting material, the corresponding optical form could be synthesized. In a comparison of the optical activities of the synthetic compound with the naturally occurring ethers, it was apparent that the D form was the predominant one.

C. Cholesterol Esters

Structure and Occurrence

The cholesterol esters are of considerable interest to biochemists and medical scientists. This is because of the concern with the level of cholesterol in the plasma and the influence that the various types of fatty acids in the diet may have upon this level. This level is considered in many circles to be directly related to atherosclerosis.

In the mammal there are three main sites of location of the cholesterol esters: the adrenals, liver, and plasma. In the adrenals, the esters represent nearly 90 per cent of the total cholesterol stores. In the plasma the cholesterol esters comprise 65 to 70 per cent of the total cholesterol. Fatty acid esters of other sterols are not normally found in any of these tissues.

Chemical Synthesis

Essentially, the preparation of fatty acid esters of cholesterol can be accomplished in a manner similar to that used for most ester syntheses with the fatty acids.

A series of cholesterol esters containing saturated fatty acids of chain length from 2 to 18 carbons and also cholesterol oleate have been synthesized in yields of 75 to 90 per cent by treating cholesterol in anhydrous pyridine with the appropriate acid chlorides at 80°C for 20 minutes.

D. Waxes

Structure and Occurrence

The lipid waxes are widely distributed in nature and occur in aquatic animals, certain plants, and micro-organisms. The lipid waxes are essentially esters of aliphatic alcohols combined with carboxylic acids. They usually contain a small amount of free fatty acid and hydrocarbons. A few hard vegetable tallows, notably bayberry wax, are included in the category of lipid waxes. Some of the lipid waxes contain polycyclic alcohols, such as sterols and triterpene alcohols, in the combined and free states.

The aliphatic alcohols involved in lipid waxes are usually normal saturated monohydric alcohols having an even number of carbons ranging from C_{10} to C_{44}, although seldom are alcohols encountered which have more than 32 carbons. Jojoba wax, expressed from the seeds of *Simmondsia chinensis* (californica), is one of the few known liquid waxes. It has, as a lipid component, esters of unsaturated alcohols (C_{20}–C_{26}) combined with unsaturated fatty acids (C_{16}–C_{22}).

Biological Relevance

Glycerides

The main function of triglycerides is to act as energy reserves both in animals and plants. In certain species the triglycerides may be replaced as energy reserves by other lipids, i.e., by waxes, acids, and also the hydrocarbon squalene. However, in general, triglycerides are the lipid most frequently involved in long-term energy storage. They produce more calories per gram than either carbohydrate or protein.

Triglycerides are also deposited subcutaneously in warm-blooded animals. Thus marine animals have fat deposited to insulate them against heat loss. Among fish which spend most of their lives in the upper water, the reserve fat is deposited in the skeletal musculature where it replaces water. The fish which live at the bottom of the sea deposit their fat almost exclusively in the liver. Triglycerides are also present in most tissues where they are accompanied by phospholipids. Stored glycerides, whether in the tissue or laid down in a depot, have been described as 'variable' elements, whilst the phospholipids, which are essential components of cell structure, are the 'constant' elements. During fasting the triglyceride is depleted but the phospholipids, being part of the structural material of the cells, are not used as reserve supplies of energy.

Animals are able to synthesize glycerides from other dietary constituents, chiefly carbohydrate and protein. This is done mainly in the liver and between the liver and the depots there is a continuous interchange. Deposited glycerides, being continually replaced by fresh supplies, pass to the liver where they may be degraded with production of energy or, alternatively, after hydrolysis and re-esterification, they are again returned to the depot.

The nature of the stored glycerides depends on the relative amounts of the synthesized and dietary material. These vary with the species of the animal, with its rate of growth and on the quality and quantity of the diet. The composition of the synthesized glycerides probably depends mainly on the species of the animal. Dietary glycerides may be modified before being laid down in the depots: there is evidence that hydrogenation sometimes occurs, and it is known that the shorter-chain acids are preferentially metabolized and seldom find their way into the depot fats. Animals are unable to synthesize certain polyethenoid acids (such as linoleic acid) considered to be essential for growth.

The liver is believed to play an important role in glyceride catabolism since it is predominantly to this organ that the glycerides are transported when carbohydrate metabolism is subnormal. The glycerides are first hydrolysed, the glycerol is converted to glucose via phosphoglycerol and triose phosphate, or metabolized along with other carbohydrates, and the fatty acids are degraded to a two-carbon unit consisting of some form of 'active' acetate which either interacts with oxaloacetate and is degraded to carbon dioxide via the tricarboxylic acid cycle, or alternatively reacts with itself to form acetoacetate which gives rise to ketone bodies. Some acetoacetate is also formed directly. These changes are shown

$$\text{Glycerides} \rightleftharpoons \text{Glycerol} + \text{Fatty Acid} \rightleftharpoons \text{Acetoacetate}$$
$$\updownarrow \quad\quad \updownarrow \quad\quad \text{CO}_2 + \text{H}_2\text{O}$$
$$\text{Glucose} \quad \text{'C}_2 \text{ unit'}$$

The study of the digestion and absorption of dietary fat is an important contemporary problem. It is known that dietary fat is largely absorbed (> 90 per cent) provided that it melts below body temperature, but that higher melting fats are only poorly absorbed. Melting point, however, is not the only criterion. The water-insoluble character of the dietary triglycerides requires special mechanisms for its absorption and transport in the organism.

Along with other food, fat passes into the stomach. It is not chemically changed here until it comes under the influence of pancreatic and intestinal lipases and of bile salts. These powerful lypolytic enzymes hydrolyse triglycerides via di- and monoglycerides to glycerol and free acid. The micellar properties of bile salts are involved in this. The solubilizing power for the polar lipids, such as the fatty acids and monoglycerides which are released from the dietary triglycerides, plays an important rôle in this process. Formerly this reaction was considered to be virtually complete before absorption occurred, but it is now known that bile salts, monoglycerides, and acids together are able to convert unhydrolysed fat into such a fine emulsion that this may be absorbed, passing through the intestinal wall and via the thoracic duct into the bloodstream and thence to the fat depots. Free acids were believed to find their way into the portal vein and to the liver, but it is now probable that this only occurs with the lower fatty acids ($< C_{16}$). The long-chain acids are predominantly absorbed via the lymphatic vessels mainly as triglycerides. Thus part of the dietary fat is digested by pancreatic and intestinal lipases and the products of hydrolysis emulsify the remainder so finely that it can pass through the intestinal wall without previous hydrolysis. The transport form of the dietary lipids are particles called chylomicrons. These are lipoproteins. The present picture of triglyceride metabolism is shown in Fig. 3.11.

Various theories have been proposed to explain the divergence in the depot fats laid down by various species of animals. One theory is based upon a simplification in the structure of fats which conforms to the increasing complexity of the animal. An alternative theory ascribes importance to the ingested fat and less to the ability of the animal to lay down its own typical fat.

Cholesterol esters

In the esters of the liver, linoleic acid is the major polyunsaturated component, with almost negligible amounts of trienoic, tetraenoic, and pentaenoic acids present. Even in dietary states where linoleic acid is fed in amounts equivalent to 30 per cent corn oil, the content of these polyunsaturated fatty acids never exceeds 36 per cent. However, with the plasma cholesterol esters, the distribution pattern is entirely different. On the lowest linoleic acid intake, the amount of polyunsaturated fatty acids in the ester is nearly 39 per cent, whereas on the highest linoleic acid diet the value rises to

102 per cent. At the same time, a very significant rise in the tetra-enoic acid content (to 36 per cent) occurs. This indicates a probable difference in the equilibrium pattern between liver and plasma compounds. Studies of α-lipoproteins have shown that free cholesterol and cholesterol esters are readily exchangeable. At the present time there is, however, little clear-cut evidence about the essential function of the cholesterol esters.

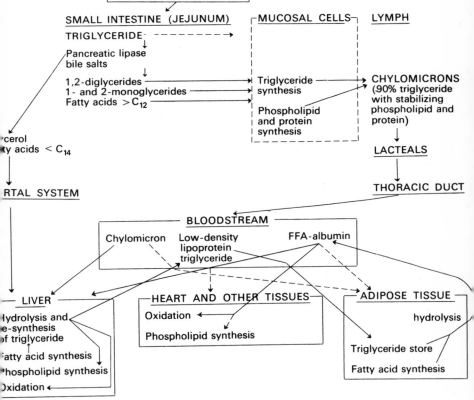

Fig. 3.11. *The metabolism of triglycerides*
(G. B. Ansell and J. N. Hawthorne, *Phospholipids*,
Vol. 3, p. 179, Elsevier Publishing Co., 1964.)

In atherosclerotic lesions (xanthomata—a skin lesion), as a result of dietary treatment which raises serum cholesterol levels in experimental animals, the percentage of 18:1 acids in the cholesterol ester is raised. Hence the cholesterol ester 18:1 becomes the major cholesterol ester whilst normally, e.g., in plasma, cholesterol ester 18:2 is the major ester.

Waxes

In nature waxes occur on the cuticle of leaves and fruit or in the secretion of insects. They usually contain smaller proportions of the free acid in alcohol and sometimes of aliphatic hydrocarbons as well as the true wax esters. The alcohol and acid components of waxes are of somewhat greater chain length than corresponding components of other lipid classes. They can serve instead of triglycerides as a main depot lipid of a plant or animal. In these cases the wax is made from shorter-chain acids and alcohols and is unsaturated. Wax replaces triglyceride fairly commonly in the depot lipids of aquatic animals. The depot fat of the sperm of whale is an example of this. The main widespread function of wax esters seems to be as a protective coating on the surface of organisms against water loss.

Further reading

General

D. Chapman, *The Structure of Lipids.* Methuen, 1965.
H. J. Deuel, *The Lipides*, Vol. I and II. Interscience, 1951.
D. J. Hanahan, *Lipide Chemistry.* J. Wiley, New York, 1960.
T. P. Hilditch and P. N. Williams, *The Chemical Constitution of Fats.* Chapman & Hall, 1964.

Special Aspects—Synthesis and Biosynthesis

T. Malkin and T. H. Bevan, *Progress in the Chemistry of Fats and Other Lipids*, **4**, 63 (1957).
F. H. Mattson and R. A. Volpenhein, *J. Lipid Research*, **3**, 281 (1962).

Insect Waxes

P. G. Fast, *Memoirs Entomological Society of Canada*, **37**, 21 (1964).

Physical Properties

D. Chapman, *Chem. Rev.*, **62**, 433 (1962).
G. L. Gaines, *Insoluble Monolayers at Liquid-gas Interfaces.* Interscience, 1966.

Digestion

B. Borgstrom, *Lipid Metabolism*, ed. K. Bloch. J. Wiley, New York, 1960.

4. Phosphoglycerides

Many of the complex lipids found in nature contain phosphorus, and these phospholipids, or phosphatides, are based either on glycerol (phosphoglycerides) or on sphingosine (sphingolipids). In this chapter we shall discuss the phosphoglycerides. These have the general structure shown below:

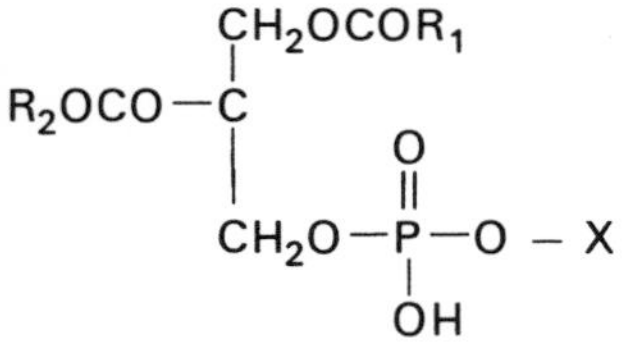

$$CH_2OCOR_1 \qquad (1)$$
$$R_2OCO-\overset{\displaystyle |}{\underset{\displaystyle |}{C}} \qquad\qquad (2)$$
$$CH_2O-\overset{O}{\overset{\|}{P}}-O-X \qquad (3)$$
$$\overset{|}{OH}$$

(R_1R_2 = fatty alkyl groups
X = base, sugar, etc.)

All natural phosphoglycerides are optically active and, with one exception, have been shown to belong to the same enantiomeric series. To prove the stereochemical configuration of natural phosphoglyceride synthetic compounds were prepared.

The naturally occurring phospholipids are, therefore, widely described as L-α- or L-3-compounds. There is, however, some confusion in the nomenclature. Since D-1,2-diglyceride is obtained on dephosphorylation, the same compounds are occasionally referred to as D-1-derivatives. Similar confusion still persists if the absolute notation system of Cahn–Ingold–Prelog is used for the designation of configuration; natural phosphoglycerides thus have the (R)-configuration at C-2 of the glyceryl residue, but the diglycerides obtained from them on dephosphorylation have the (S) configuration.*

---

* Very recently, the IUPAC–IUB Commission on Biochemical Nomenclature has published new proposals on the nomenclature of lipids, including phosphoglycerides. These are based on a system of 'stereospecific numbering' which eliminates the confusion referred to above. Details of the new draft proposals are given in the Appendix.

The amino acids contained in phospholipids belong to the natural L-series. The inositol derivatives are all based on myoinositol-phosphate with L-1 (or S) configuration. The numbering for the acyl groups is the same as with the glycerides.

The glycero-phosphate residue (a) is common to the structure of all natural phosphoglycerides. The 1,2-diacyl derivatives (b) are the most abundant and are commonly referred to as the L-3-phosphatidyl derivatives. The 1-mono-acyl derivatives (c) are called the lysophosphatidyl derivatives. The 'plasmalogens', otherwise known as L-3-phosphatidal derivatives, (d) have been found in animal tissues but not in plant lipids. No trivial names have been suggested for 1-alkyl-2-acyl (e) and the cyclic acetal (f) structures.

The substituents on positions 1 and 2 of glycerol are derived from long-chain fatty acids; the extent of variation in the chain length and unsaturation in these, and the biological significance of the variations, will be discussed in a later section. Considerable diversity has also been found in the nature of the group —X and is illustrated by the structures of some phosphatidyl derivatives in Fig. 4.1.

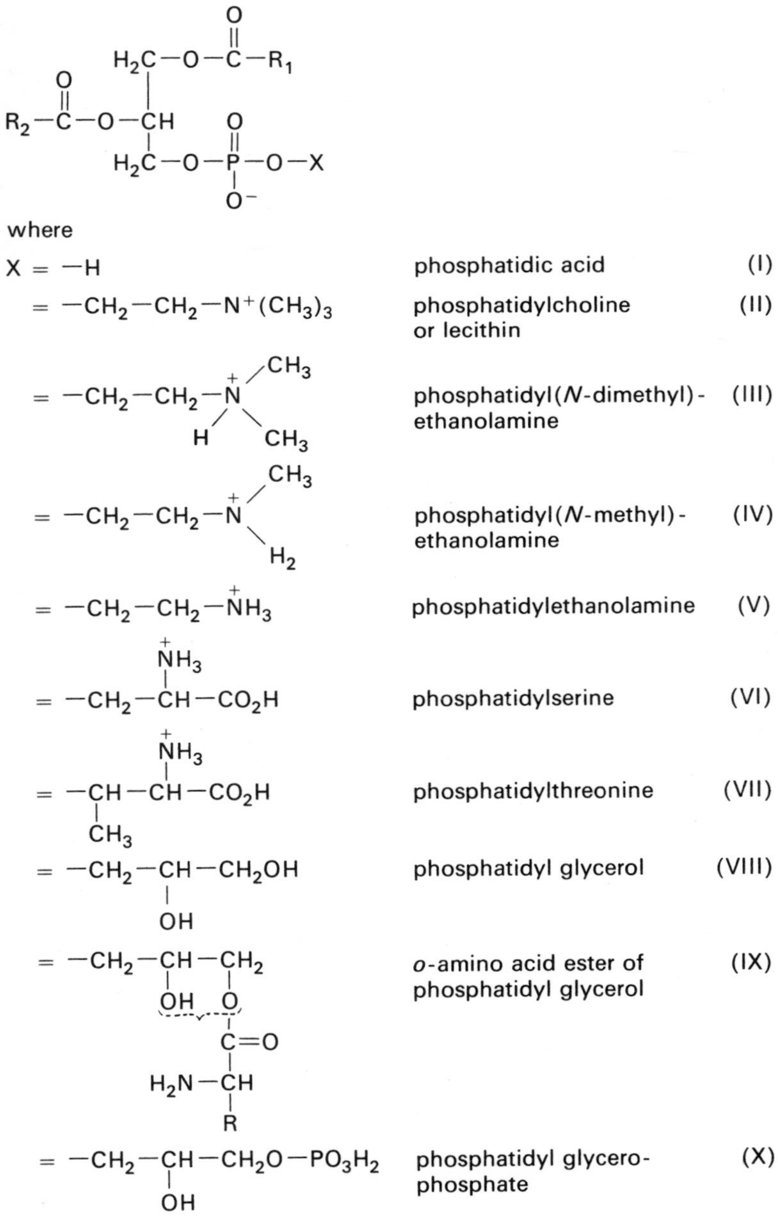

where

X = —H	phosphatidic acid	(I)
= —CH$_2$—CH$_2$—N$^+$(CH$_3$)$_3$	phosphatidylcholine or lecithin	(II)
= —CH$_2$—CH$_2$—N$^+$(CH$_3$)(H)(CH$_3$)	phosphatidyl(N-dimethyl)-ethanolamine	(III)
= —CH$_2$—CH$_2$—N$^+$(CH$_3$)(H$_2$)	phosphatidyl(N-methyl)-ethanolamine	(IV)
= —CH$_2$—CH$_2$—$\overset{+}{N}$H$_3$	phosphatidylethanolamine	(V)
= —CH$_2$—CH(NH$_3^+$)—CO$_2$H	phosphatidylserine	(VI)
= —CH(NH$_3^+$)—CH(CH$_3$)—CO$_2$H	phosphatidylthreonine	(VII)
= —CH$_2$—CH(OH)—CH$_2$OH	phosphatidyl glycerol	(VIII)
= —CH$_2$—CH(OH)—CH$_2$—O—C(=O)—CH(NH$_2$)—R	o-amino acid ester of phosphatidyl glycerol	(IX)
= —CH$_2$—CH(OH)—CH$_2$O—PO$_3$H$_2$	phosphatidyl glycero-phosphate	(X)

Fig. 4.1. *The structures of natural phosphoglycerides*

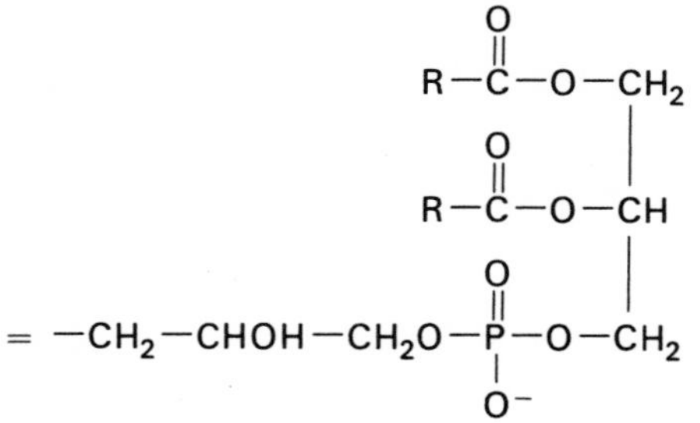

$$R-\overset{\overset{O}{\|}}{C}-O-CH_2$$

$$R-\overset{\overset{O}{\|}}{C}-O-CH$$

$= -CH_2-CHOH-CH_2O-\overset{\overset{O}{\|}}{\underset{O^-}{P}}-O-CH_2$ diphosphatidyl   (XI) 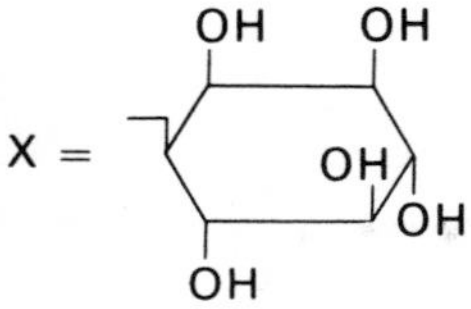
glycerol

X =   phosphatidyl(myo)inositol   (XII)
or monophosphoinositide

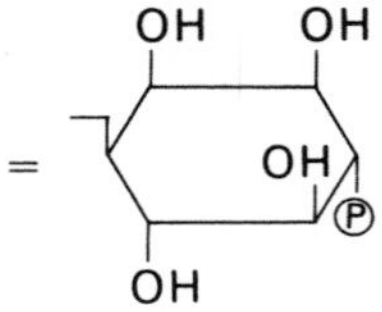

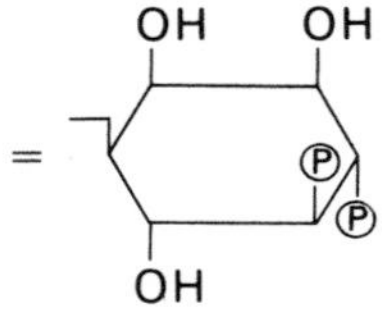

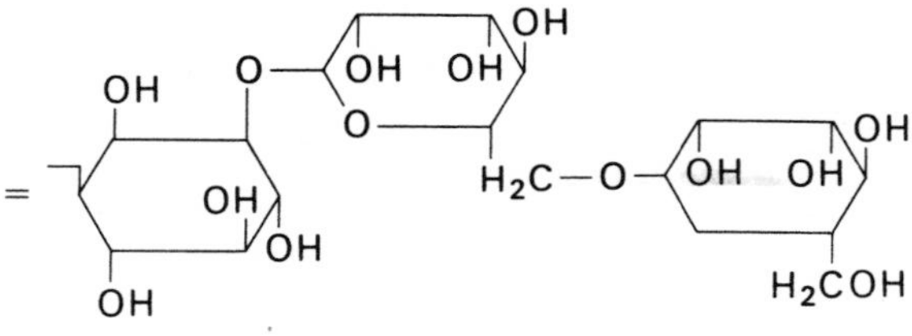

=   phosphatidyl(myo)-   (XIII)
inositol-4-phosphate or
diphosphoinositide

=   phosphatidyl(myo)-   (XIV)
inositol-4,5-diphosphate or
triphosphoinositide

=   phosphatidyl(myo)-   (XV)
inositoldimannoside

If possibility of internal salt formation does not exist (structures VIII to XV), the phosphate anion may be bound to a metal cation.
Ⓟ = phosphate

Fig. 4.1 (continued). *The structures of natural phosphoglycerides*

The simplest member of this class is phosphatidic acid (I) which has been detected in small concentrations and is known to be a dynamic key intermediate in the biosynthesis of other phosphoglycerides and glycerides. The most prominent phospholipid of nearly all the mammalian membranes is usually referred to as lecithin or phosphatidylcholine (II). *N*-mono and *N*-dimethylethanolamine-containing phosphoglycerides (III) and (IV) have been shown to act as intermediates in the conversion of phosphatidylethanolamine (V) into phosphatidylcholine. The first amino acid containing phosphoglyceride to be recognized was phosphatidylserine (VI) isolated from ox brain. Threonine has also been identified as a constituent of phosphoglycerides (VII). Phosphatidyl glycerol was discovered recently in chloroplasts (VIII). It is present in low amounts in animal tissues, but is present in high amounts in the phospholipid fraction of many bacteria. Recently, amino-acid derivatives of this polyglycerol phospholipid were discovered and obtained from *Cl. welchii* and other bacteria. This phospholipid type has the structure shown in (IX) (see p. 102 for discussion). Phosphatidylglycerophosphate (X) was recently detected in liver and is considered to act as an intermediate in the biosynthesis of phosphatidylglycerol. Phosphatidylglycerol is thought to be an intermediate in the biosynthesis of cardiolipin which has been shown to have the structure diphosphatidylglycerol (XI).

A number of inositol-containing phosphoglycerides (XII–XIV) have also been shown to exist and polyphosphateinositides have been found to occur in brain tissue. Mycobacteria have been shown to contain phosphatidyl-inositol-oligo-glycosides as well as other analogues (XV).

From the list shown in Fig. 4.1 it can be seen that there is an enormous variation in the nature of the polar head groups associated with the natural phosphoglycerides and that some of these molecules can be particularly complex. As well as this variation in polar groups each class of phosphoglyceride is associated with a considerable variation in the fatty acids. Several hundreds of different types of fatty acids have now been shown to occur in nature. Most phosphoglycerides contain an appropriate amount of saturated fatty acids having a chain length between 12 and 26 carbon atoms including some odd-numbered members. In general stearic and palmitic acids serve as major fatty acid constituents of mammalian phospholipids. Branched-chain fatty acids are also known to be quite widespread in occurrence. Unsaturated fatty acids are also found to be associated with the phospholipids. These include oleic, linoleic, linolenic, and palmitoleic acids. It has been shown that unsaturated fatty acids are usually located preferentially at the 2-position in the lecithin molecule. The fatty acids associated with the phospholipids have been shown to exhibit a certain degree of similarity in homologous tissues of different animals. Thus there is a similar fatty acid pattern from lung and brain tissue of a number of species.

No polyunsaturated fatty acids have been found in bacterial phospholipids. Typically, gram-positive bacteria contain branched fatty acids as major fatty acids and gram-negative bacteria contain straight-chain saturated and mono-unsaturated acids (branched fatty acids have been reported in a few gram-negative bacteria). The 19- and 17-carbon cyclopropane acids (*cis* 11,12-methylene octadecanoic acid and *cis* 9,10-methylene hexadecanoic acids) have not been identified in *all* gram-negative bacteria, but, since they are synthesized from the corresponding mono-unsaturated acid, they occur with the typical gram-negative fatty acid pattern. However, lactobacilli are gram-positive bacteria and contain straight chain-saturated and mono-unsaturated acids together with the cyclo-propane acids.

The phospholipases

The phospholipases are rapidly becoming one of the more useful tools in the analysis of phospholipids, and they also have applications in synthetic work. These are enzymes which effect hydrolysis specifically at only one type of ester linkage in the phosphoglyceride structure. Thus phospholipase A attacks the 2-acyloxyglycerol link; this is shown schematically in the structure below along with the positions attacked by other phospholipases, Fig. 4.2.

Phospholipase A has been detected in a wide variety of animal and a few plant tissues, but the usual sources are snake or bee and wasp venom and pancreatic extracts. Phospholipase A releases the fatty acid from the 2-acyloxy group in L-glycerophosphatides, including lecithins, cephalins, phosphatidic acid, cardiolipin, phosphatidyl inositol, and the corresponding plasmalogen analogues. There is some doubt about the 100 per cent positional specificity of this enzyme. The enzyme needs calcium ions for activity and the

hydrolytic degradation, which has an optimum pH of 7·2, can be
effected in ethereal or aqueous media.

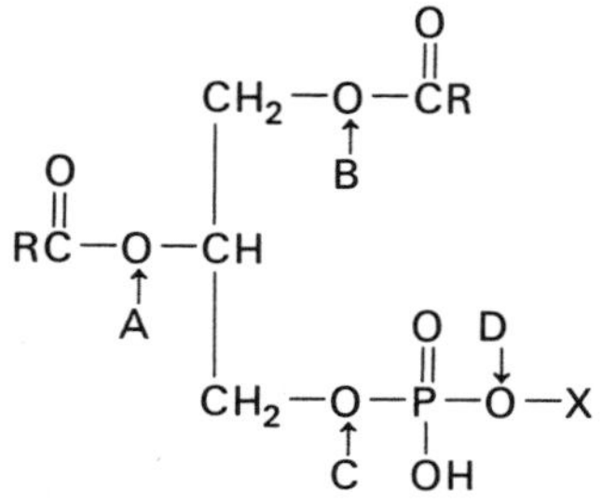

$$
\begin{array}{c}
\overset{\displaystyle O}{\underset{\displaystyle \uparrow}{\underset{\displaystyle B}{\text{CH}_2-\text{O}-\overset{\displaystyle \|}{\text{C}}\text{R}}}} \\
\end{array}
$$

Fig. 4.2. *Possible sites of enzymatic hydrolysis of phosphoglycerides*

Phospholipase B, usually obtained from animal sources such as
the pancreas, catalyses the hydrolysis of the 2-lyso phosphatides.
Phospholipase B isolated from *Penicillium notatum*, was considered
to be specific for the hydrolysis of lysophosphatides. However, under
certain conditions, it can directly degrade diacyl phosphatides to
the glycerol phosphate esters.

The function of phospholipase A and B appears after secretion
into the duodenum to digest dietary phospholipids. The phospholipase A in intestinal mucosa is quite different in character to that
of the pancreas. The same enzyme may be present in brain.

Phospholipase C appears to be mainly confined to the bacterial
kingdom and is obtained from bacterial cultures such as *Clostridium
welchii*. It hydrolyses unsaturated lecithins to diglycerides and
choline phosphate—the more active phospholipase C from *Bacillus
cereus* will also hydrolyse phosphatidylethanolamine and other
phosphoglycerides.

Phospholipase D, readily obtained from a variety of plant tissues,
especially of the cabbage family, is known to hydrolyse saturated
and unsaturated phosphatides to phosphatidic acid in good yields.

Pathways leading to the degradation of lecithin are summarized
in Fig. 4.3. It will be noted that lecithin may be broken down by
three different pathways, initiated by phospholipase A, phospholipase C, or phospholipase D. In animal tissues lecithin is converted into lysolecithin, glycerylphosphorylcholine (GPC), glycero-
phosphate, and glycerol by the successive actions of phospholipase
A, phospholipase B, GPC diesterase, and phosphomonoesterase.

In bacteria phospholipase C converts lecithin into diglyceride and phosphorylcholine which is further hydrolysed by phosphomono-esterase. In plants phospholipase D converts lecithin into choline and phosphatidic acid which is further broken down by phos-phatidic acid phosphatase.

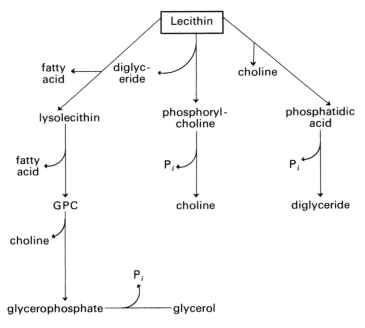

Fig. 4.3. *Degradation of lecithin*

These enzymes have been used for analytical and synthetic pur-poses. An example of the use of phospholipase A as an aid to synthesis is shown in Fig. 4.4. Synthetic dioleoyl-lecithin was degraded with snake venom phospholipase A so as to give 1-oleoyl-glycero-3-phosphorylcholine. After introduction of tritium, the lysocompound was acylated so as to give 1-[9 . 10 . ^{3}H]-stearoyl-2-[1 . ^{14}C]-stearoyl-glycero-3-phosphorylcholine.

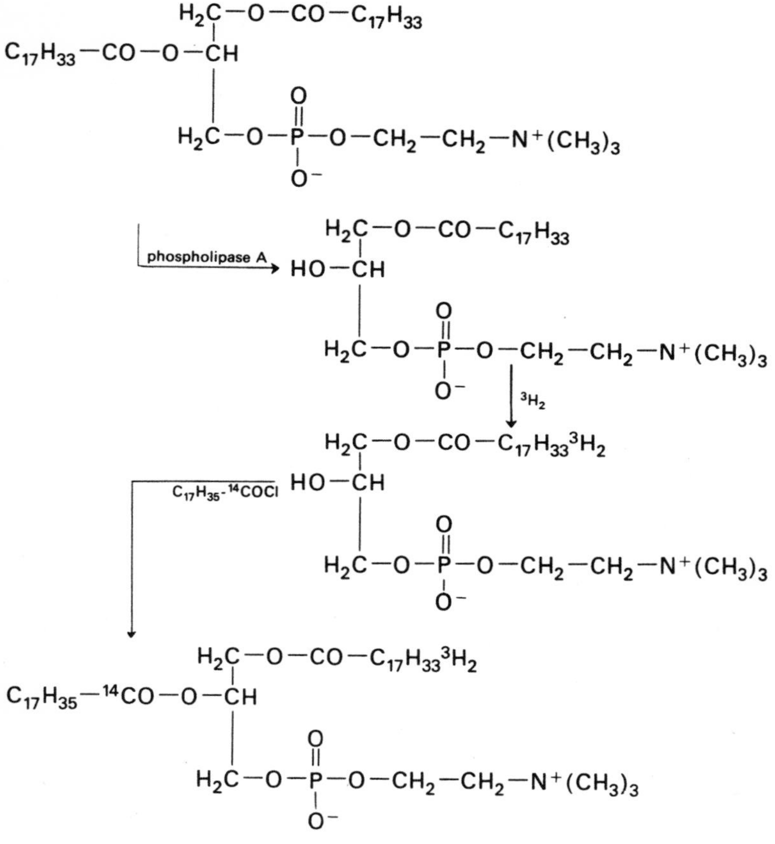

Fig. 4.4. The use of phospholipase A in synthesis

Structure Determination

Chromatographic behaviour

Qualitative and quantitative analysis of phospholipid mixtures can readily be made using paper or thin-layer chromatography. Paper chromatography is now regarded as the less useful of the two techniques. However, good separations of phosphatides can be obtained on silicic-acid impregnated filter paper or glass paper, using diisobutyl ketone–acetic acid–water eluent.

Tricomplex staining (which can be made quantitative by densito-metric analysis of the spots or by phosphorus analysis of the excised spots) is often used as a detection agent, since it gives specific colorations with the various phospholipid classes. Complex inosite mixtures can be separated on formalin impregnated paper.

Thin-layer chromatography on silica gel has been applied to the separation of phospholipid and sphingolipid mixtures, using chloroform–methanol–water mixtures as eluents. The rapid technique of thin-layer chromatography using micro slides is most convenient, allowing a total qualitative analysis to be effected in a few minutes. The lipids are visualized by specific spray reagents (see Table 4.1) and they can be quantitatively estimated, either by densitometric measurement of the spots after charring, or by analysis of the excised spots.

Hydrolysis reactions

The fatty ester linkages of phospholipids are hydrolysed very slowly at pH 7, somewhat faster in acidic media, but very rapidly in alkaline media. Alcoholysis is similarly pH dependent, although the rate is slower than for hydrolysis. These hydrolysis methods are often employed in analysis, e.g., the fatty acid methyl esters are quantitatively recovered for gas–liquid chromatography after methanolysis of the phospholipid sample with dry hydrogen chloride in excess methanol. Alkaline hydrolysis with alcoholic sodium hydroxide gives the water-soluble phosphate esters which can be separated and identified.

Examples of structure determination

Products of partial hydrolysis are more informative than those obtained by complete rupture of all the ester linkages. Partial hydrolysis can now be conveniently achieved by enzymatic action using specific phospholipases. In the original studies, chemical hydrolysis which lacks specificity akin to lipolysis was employed. The derivation of structure based on the identity of water-soluble hydrolysis products requires caution. The interpretation is illustrated below, Fig. 4.5.

Hydrolysis of lecithin with alkali gave fatty acid (2 moles), choline (1 mole) and glycerol phosphate (1 mole). The reaction proceeds by a rapid hydrolysis of the two fatty ester linkages and the initial product is glycerophosphorylcholine (GPC). The choline–phosphate link in GPC is, however, not as resistant to hydrolytic cleavage as is the case with other simple dialkylphosphates and GPC

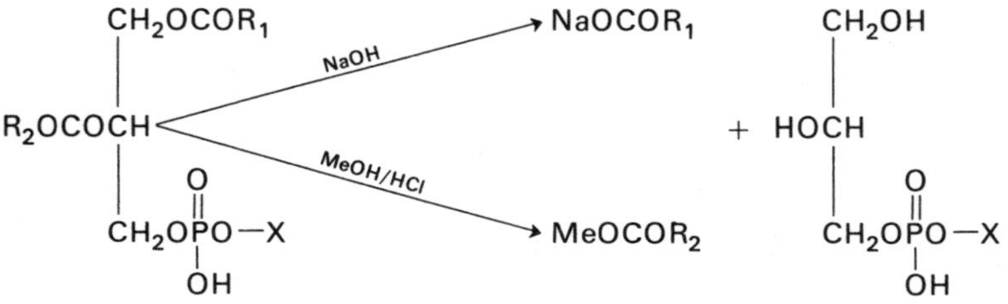

Fig. 4.5. Hydrolysis reactions with phospholipids

breaks down further to yield glycerolphosphate and choline. The labilizing effect is derived from participation of the neighbouring 2-hydroxyl group of glycerol and the first step is essentially a disdisplacement reaction.

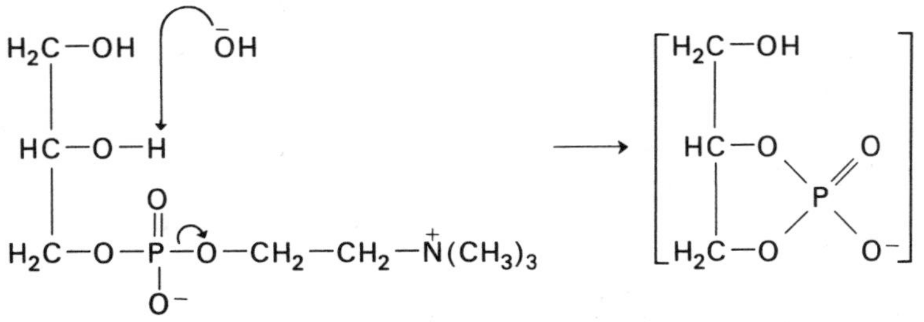

Subsequently, the cyclic phosphate ring in the intermediate reopens at either of the two alternative sites to yield a mixture of glycerol-3-phosphate and glycerol-2-phosphate. The latter is thus an artefact but its presence in the hydrolysate was originally regarded as evidence for the presence of 2-lecithins (diacyl-glycero-2-phosphorylcholines) in nature, in addition to the 3-lecithins.

The above attack by OH^- on the asymmetric 2-position, leading to glycerol-3-phosphate may proceed by inversion of configuration. In addition, in acid solution, an equilibrium exists between the 3- and the 2-phosphates. Consequently, the product isolated from natural (optically active) lecithin is a mixture of racemates of 3- and 2-glycerolphosphate. Thus examination of the hydrolysis products does not lead to an unequivocal structure for lecithins. A similar situation exists for other phosphoglycerides.

For natural lecithin, the decision between 3-phosphate and 2-phosphate linkage and proof of the stereochemical configuration was finally obtained by other means. By comparison with the optical rotation, X-ray diffraction patterns and other physical properties of optically pure synthetic lecithins, with natural lecithin, the latter was assigned the structure of diacyl-L-3-glycerophosphorylcholine.

For the most part, the techniques used in the structure determination of phospholipids are not unique to this group. This is apparent from the data in Table 4.1.

Phosphatidyl myoinositol

An example of the chemical processes required for the determination of the structure of complex phospholipids is illustrated by studies on the phospholipids present in mycobacteria.

Mycobacteria such as *Mycobacterium tuberculosis* and *Mycobacterium phlei* have been found to contain myoinositol-containing phospholipids in which the myoinositol ring is substituted with varying amounts of D-mannose.

These phospholipids were first extracted with a mixture of chloroform and methanol after drying and defatting the cells with

Table 4.1. Methods for phospholipid structure determination

Method	Information
Thin-layer chromatography (TLC)	Qualitative and quantitative analyses
Spot tests	Functional groups
Hydrolysis and paper chromatography of water solubles	Determination of phospholipid type
IR spectra	Determination of lipid class
Methanolysis or hydrolysis then GLC of methyl esters	Total fatty acid composition
Methanolysis or hydrolysis then GLC of methyl esters upon each TLC spot	Fatty acid composition of each lipid class
Phospholipase hydrolysis then GLC of free and bound fatty acids	Distribution of fatty acids between 1 and 2 positions
Acetolysis to diglyceride acetate and investigation of these by TLC on silver nitrate impregnated plates	Distribution of fatty acids between 1 and 2 positions of any glycerophosphate
Periodic acid oxidation	Vicinal glycols
Metallic salts and complexes	Lecithin ($CdCl_2$ adduct) acidic phospholipids (lead salts)
Dinitrofluorobenzene complexes	Primary amines
Acylation products	Amino and hydroxy function
Molecular rotation	Optical purity
Titration with acid and bases in non-aqueous media	Determination of lipid type and purity

acetone. The chromatogram of the deacylation product shows the existence of a number of myoinositol-containing components each of which also contains glycerol and phosphate. These are the glyceryl–phosphoryl–myoinositol mannosides which have become water soluble due to removal of the fatty acids. These substances are isolated by paper chromatography or by column chromatography on DEAE-Sephadex.

Myoinositol is the skeleton of the widely occurring phosphatidyl-myoinositol. The structure was established by the chemical methods outlined in Fig. 4.6.

The phospholipids were shown to be derivatives of phosphatidyl-myoinositol by the kind of reactions given in Fig. 4.7. This shows the

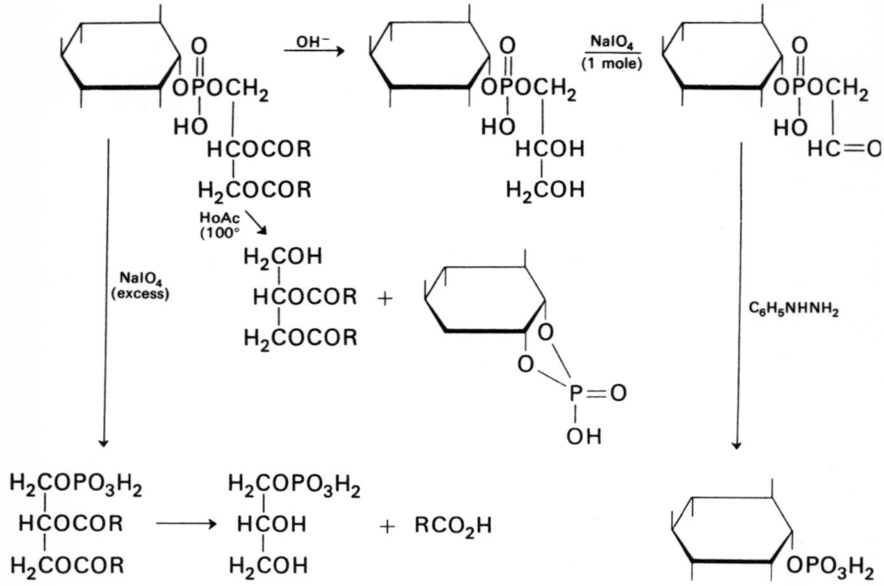

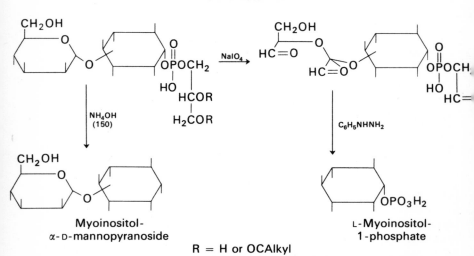

Fig. 4.6. Scheme of reactions by which phosphatidyl-myoinositol was characterized

Myoinositol-
α-D-mannopyranoside

L-Myoinositol-
1-phosphate

R = H or OCAlkyl

Fig. 4.7. Reactions outlining the partial characterization of glyceryl-phosphoryl-myoinositol monomannoside

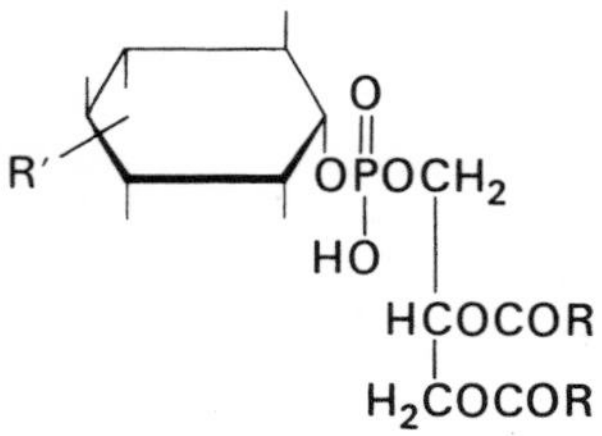

R = Fatty acid chains
I. R′ = H
II. R′ = α-D-Mannoside
III. R′ = Dimannoside
IV. R′ = Trimannoside
V. R′ = Tetramannoside
VI. R′ = Pentamannoside

Fig. 4.8. Illustration of the phosphatidyl-myoinositol structure common to all of the mycobacterial phosphoinositides

way in which the phosphate group, and therefore the phosphatidyl group, is attached to the same position on the myoinositol ring in all of these lipids. The general structure of these compounds is given in Fig. 4.8.

Chemical Synthesis of Phosphoglycerides

There is now available a variety of synthetic methods for the synthesis of pure optical isomers and racemic mixtures of the various types of phosphoglycerides. We shall illustrate only a few of these synthetic methods. A fuller account will be found in the list for further reading.

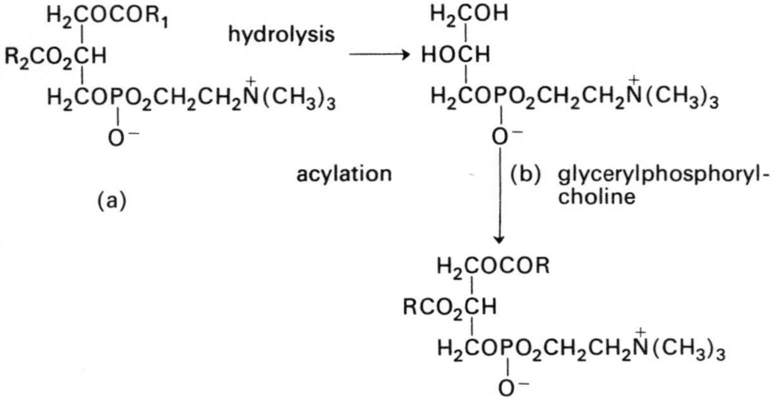

Fig. 4.9. Partial synthesis of L-lecithins containing two identical fatty acids

A convenient and very useful route to lecithins is the partial synthesis shown in Fig. 4.9. Mild alkaline hydrolysis of crude preparations of natural lecithin (e.g., from egg yolk) yields glycerylphosphorylcholine, readily purified as its cadmium complex. Acylation of the complex yields lecithins with any desired fatty acyl residues.

To obtain lecithins containing two different acyl residues, two additional steps are necessary. Treatment of a lecithin (containing two identical fatty acids) with phospholipase A causes hydrolysis at the 2-position only. The 1-acyl lyso derivative thus formed is then reacylated (preferably as its cadmium chloride complex) with the chloride of a fatty acid different from that located at the 1-position.

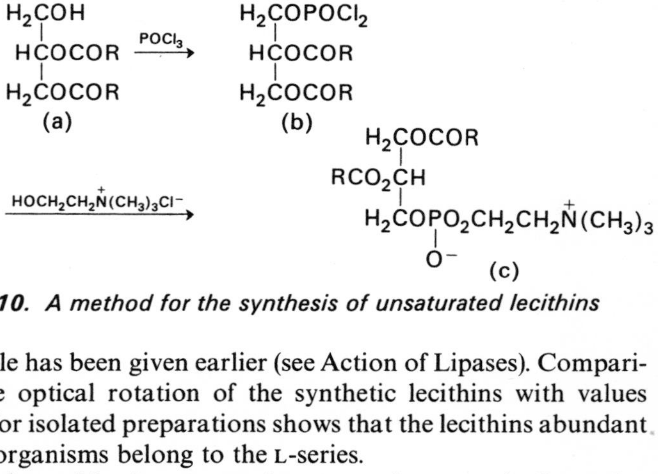

$$
\begin{array}{ccc}
\text{H}_2\text{COH} & & \text{H}_2\text{COPOCl}_2 \\
| & \xrightarrow{\text{POCl}_3} & | \\
\text{HCOCOR} & & \text{HCOCOR} \\
| & & | \\
\text{H}_2\text{COCOR} & & \text{H}_2\text{COCOR} \\
\text{(a)} & & \text{(b)}
\end{array}
$$

$$
\xrightarrow{\text{HOCH}_2\text{CH}_2\overset{+}{\text{N}}(\text{CH}_3)_3\text{Cl}^-}
$$

$$
\begin{array}{l}
\text{H}_2\text{COCOR} \\
| \\
\text{RCO}_2\text{CH} \\
| \\
\text{H}_2\text{COPO}_2\text{CH}_2\text{CH}_2\overset{+}{\text{N}}(\text{CH}_3)_3 \\
\quad\quad | \\
\quad\quad \text{O}^- \quad \text{(c)}
\end{array}
$$

Fig. 4.10. *A method for the synthesis of unsaturated lecithins*

An example has been given earlier (see Action of Lipases). Comparison of the optical rotation of the synthetic lecithins with values recorded for isolated preparations shows that the lecithins abundant in higher organisms belong to the L-series.

By starting with the appropriate racemic or optically active saturated or unsaturated diglycerides, the corresponding lecithins are obtained. This is shown in Fig. 4.10. Total synthesis may proceed by phosphorylation of diglycerides with phosphorus oxychloride in the presence of quinoline. After purification the acid dichloride (b) is esterified with choline (chloride or iodide) to obtain lecithin.

Several by-products are formed during phosphorylation with $POCl_3$. The use of monophenylphosphoryldichloride instead of $POCl_3$ gives fewer by-products, but the protecting phenyl group in the intermediate stage (c) has to be removed by catalytic hydrogenation. The method is of limited value since it gives lecithins containing saturated fatty acids. This method is shown in Fig. 4.11.

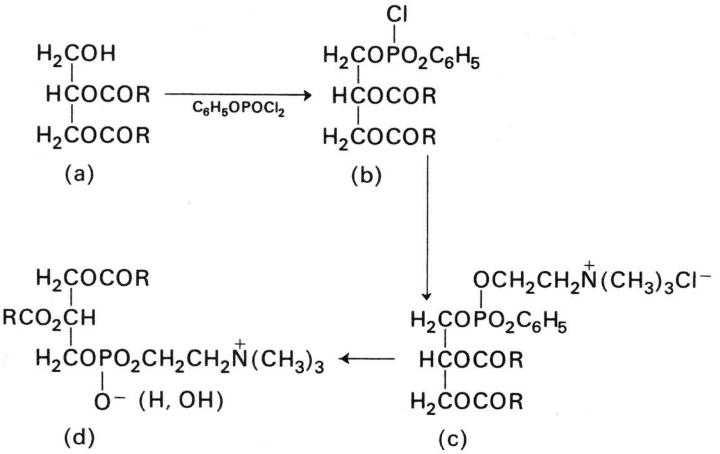

Fig. 4.11. *A synthetic method for saturated lecithins*

The partial isomerization of 1,2-diglycerides to 1,3-isomers is a recognized hazard. The use of 3,2-diacylglycerol-α-iodohydrins (or bromohydrins) is now preferred. See Fig. 4.12. The procedure involves condensation between a diacyl glycerol-α-iodohydrin (a) and silver dibenzylphosphate (b) with precipitation of silver iodide. The dibenzyl esters (c) of phosphatidic acids are thus formed which are excellent intermediates for the preparation of lecithins and also of other types of phosphatides. Thus debenzylation may be effected by using a palladium–charcoal catalyst to obtain saturated phosphatidic acids (d). On the other hand, monodebenzylation of (c), which cannot be effected by partial hydrolysis, is readily accomplished by anionic debenzylation with anhydrous sodium or barium iodide in acetone. The mono-benzyl ester on treatment with silver nitrate gives the silver salt (e) which is condensed with 2-bromo-ethyltrimethylammonium picrate. From the condensation product, the free base (f) is recovered in a reasonable yield by decomposing the picrate. The protective benzyl group may be removed either by hydrogenolysis or by anionic debenzylation, and the method is thus suitable and has been used for the synthesis of both saturated and unsaturated lecithins.

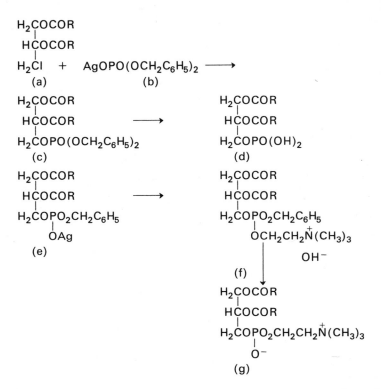

Fig. 4.12. *The synthesis of phosphatidic acids and lecithins using* α-*iodoglycerides*

The synthesis of phosphatidic acids and of lecithins through the 2,3-diacylglycerol-1-iodohydrins has been discussed above. A silver salt of the benzylphosphatidic acid is an excellent general intermediate for the synthesis of other phosphoglycerides as well. This is illustrated by the synthesis of phosphatidylethanolamine in Fig. 4.13.

A variation of the synthetic route through 2,3-diacylglycerol-1-iodohydrins is illustrated below for the synthesis of phosphatidylserine, Fig. 4.14. By the use of different phosphate moieties, other phosphoglycerides can also be obtained.

As was mentioned at the outset, the examples cited above illustrate only a few among the numerous procedures for the synthesis of phosphoglycerides which have been reported in the literature. We conclude by describing the following procedure in which a phosphite ester is first synthesized and subsquently oxidized to the phosphate.

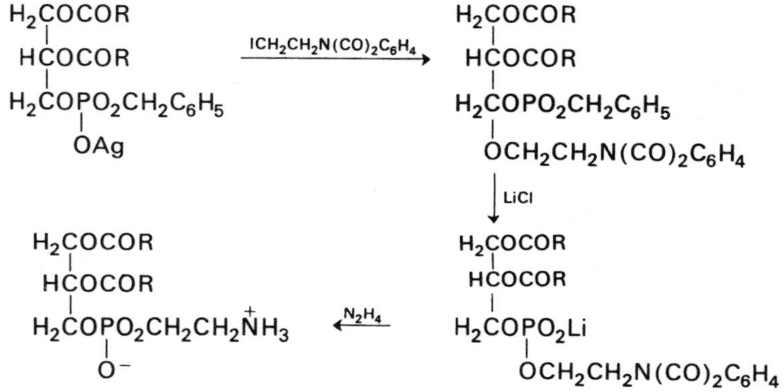

$$H_2COCOR$$
$$HCOCOR$$
$$H_2COPO_2CH_2C_6H_5$$
$$OAg$$

$$\xrightarrow{ICH_2CH_2N(CO)_2C_6H_4}$$

$$H_2COCOR$$
$$HCOCOR$$
$$H_2COPO_2CH_2C_6H_5$$
$$OCH_2CH_2N(CO)_2C_6H_4$$

$$\downarrow LiCl$$

$$H_2COCOR$$
$$HCOCOR$$
$$H_2COPO_2CH_2CH_2\overset{+}{N}H_3$$
$$O^-$$

$$\xleftarrow{N_2H_4}$$

$$H_2COCOR$$
$$HCOCOR$$
$$H_2COPO_2Li$$
$$OCH_2CH_2N(CO)_2C_6H_4$$

Fig. 4.13. The synthesis of a phosphatidylethanolamine

$$H_2COCOR$$
$$HCOCOR + AgOPO_2CH_2-CH\overset{NHOCOBz}{\underset{CO_2Bz}{}}$$
$$H_2Cl \qquad\qquad OPh$$

$$\longrightarrow$$
$$H_2COCOR$$
$$HCOCOR$$
$$H_2COPO_2CH_2CH\overset{NHOCOBz}{\underset{CO_2Bz}{}}$$
$$OPh$$

$$\xrightarrow[CH_3CO_2H]{H_2/Pt/Pd}$$

$$H_2COCOR$$
$$HCOCOR$$
$$H_2COPO_2CH_2CH-CO_2H$$
$$O^- \qquad NH_3^+$$

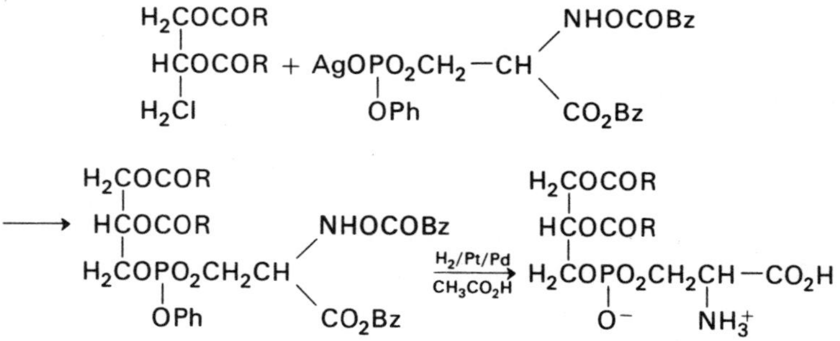

Fig. 4.14. The synthesis of a phosphatidylserine

The method was originally developed in nucleotide chemistry and is illustrated for the synthesis of phosphatidylethanolamine, but is useful for the synthesis of other types of phosphoglycerides as well. Action of O-benzylphosphorus-O,O-diphenylphosphoric acid anhydride on the diglyceride gives 2,3-diacyglycerol-α-benzyl phosphite (c). Oxidative chlorination of this compound with N-chlorosuccinimide yields the phosphorochloridate (d), which is coupled with 2-hydroxyethylphthalimide to give (e). Removal of the protecting groups by anionic debenzylation and hydrazinolysis respectively gives the corresponding phosphatidylethanolamine (f), Fig. 4.15.

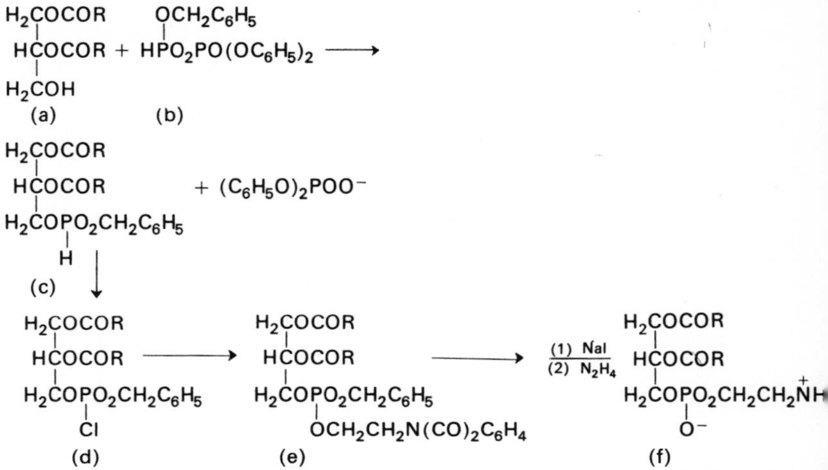

Fig. 4.15. *Phosphorylation with O-benzylphosphorus-O,O-diphenylphosphoric acid anhydride and synthesis of phosphatidylethanolamine*

Biosynthesis

The problem of the biological synthesis and breakdown of phospholipids has for decades been the subject of considerable interest and speculation. However, no progress was made in working out the pathways by which phospholipids are formed and broken down until the introduction of the isotope tracer technique.

The resemblance in structure between the common phosphoglycerides finds expression in their biological formation. A requirement for cytidine coenzymes has now been unequivocally demonstrated in the biosynthesis of at least four types of phospholipids, including phosphatidylethanolamine, phosphatidylcholine, phosphatidylinositol and phosphatidyl glycerol. Presently known pathways for the biosynthesis of phosphoglycerides are shown in Fig. 4.16.

Little is known of the metabolic pathways by which phosphatidylserine is formed *de novo*. By analogy with the other phosphoglycerides it might be expected that the formation involves such intermediates as *O*-phosphoserine, cytidine diphosphateserine and D-1,2-diglyceride. No evidence has been put forward, however, for the direct phosphorylation of serine. In fact the presence in various tissues of powerful phosphoserine phosphatases seems to indicate that phosphatidylserine is formed by a metabolic pathway different from that of phosphatidylcholine or phosphatidylethanolamine. A *de novo* synthesis of phosphatidylserine from L-serine and cytidine diphosphate diglyceride has been reported to occur in cell-free extracts of *Escherichia coli*. This reaction may also take place in mammalian tissues.

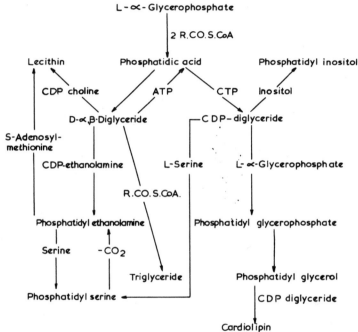

Fig. 4.16. *Biosynthetic pathways for phosphoglycerides*
(CDP = cytidine diphosphate, CTP = cytidine triphosphate)

Although available evidence indicates an equilibrium reaction to exist between phosphatidylethanolamine and L-serine, yielding phosphatidylserine and ethanolamine, this reaction probably is not a predominant pathway in the formation of phosphatidylserine, because of the rather different fatty acid composition of naturally occurring phosphatidylethanolamine and phosphatidylserine.

For the same reason the enzyme-catalysed methylation of phosphatidylethanolamine yielding phosphatidylcholine is not expected to play a predominant part in the biosynthesis of the latter in animal tissues. Compelling evidence for the occurrence of this pathway of lecithin biosynthesis has, however, been provided in a mutant strain of *Neurospora crassa*. The intermediate monomethyl- and dimethyl-aminoethanol-containing phospholipids were isolated and shown to possess the same fatty acid pattern as the lecithin ultimately formed. Whilst this pathway will occur in animal tissues, only in mammals acutely deficient in dietary choline is it expected to prevail over the usual *de novo* synthesis of phosphatidylcholine catalysed by the citidine-containing coenzyme.

Certain intermediates in the biosynthesis of one type of lipid are key-compounds also in the biochemical formation of other classes of lipids. Fatty acyl CoA for example is necessary for the formation of phosphatidic acid and triglyceride, while D-1,2-diglycerides are essential for the formation of triglycerides, see page 55, as well as for the synthesis of phosphatidylcholine and phosphatidylethanolamine. The pool of these common intermediates is usually assumed to be equally available to each of the competing enzymes. However, the lipids phosphatidylethanolamine and phosphatidycholine isolated from the same tissue usually show rather large differences in fatty acid composition. This finding can be explained by assuming that the enzyme systems which catalyse the phosphorylation of the corresponding diglycerides must possess a specificity for particular types of diglycerides.

Some differences do exist in the specificity of the enzymes involved in the formation of triglycerides and lecithins, respectively. However, it has not been sufficiently proved that the observed differences in fatty acid composition of various classes of lipids can be attributed exclusively to differences in specificity of the enzymes responsible for their formation.

A similar situation exists also for the fatty acyl CoA pool, since the constituent fatty acids of the phosphoglycerides possess both a positional and metabolic asymmetry. It has been repeatedly demonstrated that saturated and unsaturated fatty acids tend to occupy distinct locations in the lecithin molecule, and that the incorporation of a specific fatty acid varies, depending upon its structure and whether it is esterified at the 2- or 3-position.

The liver and intestines are very active sites for the synthesis of phosphoglycerides. Labelling studies have shown that almost all cells, apart from erythrocytes, possess the ability to synthesize all the individual phospholipids from fundamental building blocks, e.g., phosphate and choline, etc. It seems that each tissue is more or less an independent phospholipid building factory which receives its structural units from the plasma. With regard to the intra-cellular location of phospholipid synthesis, *in vivo* studies of the tissue show that, after homogenization and fractionation, all fractions from the cell contain radio-active phospholipids. It seems likely that synthesis is carried out in a particular location and the newly formed phospholipid is then carried to other parts of the cell, e.g., by protoplasmic streaming.

Both smooth and rough surfaced microsomal membranes possess equal abilities to synthesize lecithin despite marked differences in their content of RNA and phospholipid. When most of the RNA is extracted from the microsomes, little impairment in this lecithin synthesis occurs, which suggests that only a small proportion of the microsomal RNA is involved in lecithin formation.

Little information is available concerning the distribution of the lipases involved in phospholipid turnover. It appears that phospholipids are catabolized in each tissue rather than carried to a particular centre for digestion and disposal. There is probably some method by which newly formed phospholipid can be transported from the site of synthesis to be deposited in the organelle where phospholipid turnover is occurring. Thus it may be necessary for the lecithin synthesis in the endoplasmic reticulum to be incorporated into the lipoprotein structure of the mitochondria. As the cell organelles and inclusions are in a constant state of movement relative to the cell wall and nucleus, the method used for the redistribution of newly synthesized phospholipid may involve protoplasmic streaming and circulation. Physicochemical studies are of interest here since they suggest that free phospholipid molecules do not occur in solution when naturally occurring lecithin is added to water. Studies show that there is apparently no interchange between molecules of one phospholipid layer and those of another when they are separated by an aqueous phase.

There is no appreciable exchange between phospholipids in water and phospholipids in the lipoproteins of intact mitochondria. Experiments have shown, using labelled phospholipid incubated with mitochondria, that incorporation into the particulate matter occurs only if cholate or deoxycholate are added to disrupt the mitochondrial structure, and then only in the presence of salt. In this case a form of heterocoagulation is probably occurring rather than true exchange between the molecules of the phospholipid micro-particles and the phospholipid molecules in the disrupted mito-chondria.

There is no convincing evidence that intact molecules of phospho-lipids in plasma lipoproteins exchange with more than a small pro-portion of the phospholipid pool of the blood cells. Thus ruminant blood cells contain a negligible lecithin component in their lipo-proteins, whereas in the plasma as much as 70 per cent of the lipopro-tein is lecithin. Thus there does not appear to be a complete and ready exchange between the two phospholipid pools.

There is, however, good evidence to support the idea that an exchange of phospholipid molecules can occur between the lipo-proteins of plasma and those of the chylomicrons. The exchange is mainly between the choline-containing phospholipids of the chylo-micron and those of the high density lipoproteins in the plasma.

It cannot be precluded that, next to the pathways shown in Fig. 4.16, other biosynthetic routes must exist which afford phospholipids with a fatty acid composition that is different from that of the 1,2-diglycerides present in the tissue.

The concept of a biosynthetic mechanism allowing an indepen-dent turnover of the fatty acid moieties is now strongly supported by the finding of an enzyme-system capable of acylating lysolecithin to lecithin. This enzyme present in liver microsomes is specific for lysolecithin ; neither L-1-glycerylphosphorylcholine nor L-1-glycero-phosphoric acid can be acylated to the corresponding mono- or diacyl derivatives. Taking into account the ubiquitous occurrence of phospholipase A, an enzyme catalysing the hydrolysis of 2-attached fatty acids of glycerophosphatides, a cycle may be visualized in which a fatty acid residue is removed from the lecithin molecule, yielding lysolecithin which in turn can be reacylated with another fatty acid to form lecithin once again. Acylation of lysolecithin has been reported to occur also in brain mitochondria.

Lysophosphatidylinositol and lysophosphatidic acid can also be acylated *in vivo* to form diacyl phospholipids. The enzymic acylation of lysophosphatidylethanolamine has been reported. These enzyme-systems have been found in such different tissues as brain, liver, pancreas, and red cells. This suggests that lysophospholipids have an important rôle in the metabolism of phospholipids.

The most probable pathways of phospholipid breakdown are shown in Fig. 4.3 and Fig. 4.17.

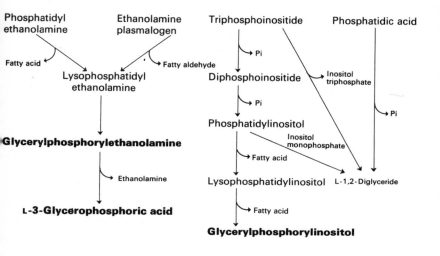

Fig. 4.17. *Pathways of breakdown for some phospholipids*

Physical Properties

Solid and mesomorphic properties

Phospholipid molecules have a number of interesting physical properties and many studies have been made especially with purified natural lecithins. Since pure individual lecithins and other phospholipids can be synthesized now, data on such materials are becoming available.

In common with other lipid molecules, phospholipids have been found to exhibit polymorphic behaviour. The crystalline form obtained is dependent on the solvent used for crystallization, and transitions from one form to another occur. Another interesting property observed with the solid lecithins and phosphatidylethanolamines, for example, is the production on heating of a mesomorphic, or liquid crystalline, phase at a certain transition temperature. Thus, whilst a phospholipid, such as distearoylglycerophosphorylethanol-amine shows true or capillary melting points above 200°C, a differential heating curve shows that the heat absorption at the capillary melting point is relatively small. This is in contrast with the larger heat change which occurs at considerably lower temperatures (110°C in Fig. 4.18).

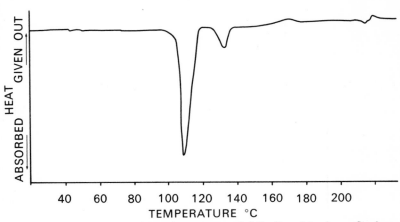

Fig. 4.18. *Differential heating curve of 1,2-dimyristoyl-* DL *-3-phos-phatidylethanolamine*

The reason for this behaviour is that the dispersion forces between the hydrocarbon chains are considerably less than the forces holding the ionic groups together. Hence the hydrocarbon chains 'melt' at a much lower temperature than do the ionic groups. The transition temperatures corresponding to this crystalline–liquid crystalline transition vary with the fatty acid residues present in the phospholipid. Thus, if one of the fatty acid residues of the phospholipid is *cis* unsaturated, the transition occurs at much lower temperatures than occurs with the fully saturated derivative. Natural phospholipids, such as exist in mitochondria, contain highly unsaturated fatty acyl residues and hence, at room temperature, are in a liquid crystalline phase, i.e., the hydrocarbon chains of these lipids are 'melted' and are in a very fluid state.

Properties in water

In the presence of water, as the amount of water increases, the transition temperature to the liquid crystal phase is lowered, but reaches a limiting value. At this temperature the phospholipids spontaneously form myelin figures; these are concentric arrangements of phospholipids organized in a bilayer structure separated by aqueous channels. An electron micrograph of a myelin figure is shown in Fig. 4.19. Globules of concentric bilayers are being used by some authors as models for membrane studies. Ions are trapped in the aqueous channels and their diffusion through the bilayers studied.

Fig. 4.19. Electron micrograph of egg lecithin dispersed in water using negative staining

Ultrasonication of unsaturated lecithins is considered by some authors to break the myelin figures into smaller fragments, whilst others have suggested that this causes the lipid to form a micellar condition. Ultrasonicated lipid reacts with various enzymes much more rapidly than the coarse aggregates (see page 103).

As the concentration of phospholipid decreases, the thickness of the aqueous layer increases. This also occurs if anionic phospholipids are present in the mixture. The presence of NaCl or KCl causes the aqueous layer to contract. The presence of CaCl$_2$ causes similar behaviour and the aqueous layer is almost eliminated.

Although, in water, pure lecithins appear to give only lamellar types of structure, other types of organization can occur with polar lipids. A sample of brain lipid in water shows two liquid crystalline structures, the lamellar and the hexagonal phases. Whether phase transitions from one phase to another have any biological relevance is still under discussion at the present time. The diacyl phosphatidylethanolamines appear to form more than one type of phase in water.

In the liquid crystalline phase in water, unsaturated lecithins, e.g., natural egg yolk lecithin, solubilize large quantities of cholesterol. This has been studied using microscope and X-ray methods. A typical phase diagram is shown in Fig. 4.20. It can be seen that up to 33 per cent cholesterol (corresponding to a molecular ratio of 1:1 with lecithin) can be solubilized by the lecithin. The zones of various phases are shown in the diagram. The presence of cholesterol causes a slight increase in the X-ray long-spacing associated with the lipid.

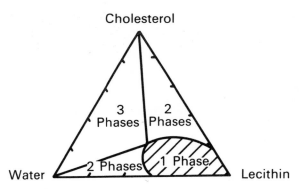

Fig. 4.20. *The phase diagram for lecithin/cholesterol/water*

There is a variety of groups associated with the phospholipids covering a wide range of pK values. Some of these are shown in Table 4.2. The lecithin molecules are considered to be isoelectric over a wide pH range, and to form zwitterion type structures. (A particular feature of cell membranes is their low surface charge density. Most cell membranes contain large quantities of lecithin or choline-containing phospholipids.) The presence of functional groups such

Table 4.2. Ionic species of naturally occurring lipids

Ionic species	Example	Remarks
Primary phosphate (PO_4^{2-})	Phosphatidic acid	Strongly acid pK_1 3·9 with secondary pK_2 8·3 valency dissociating at pH 7·5
Secondary phosphate (PO_4^-)	Monophosphoinositide Cardiolipin	Strong acid pK < 2
Amine ($-\overset{+}{N}H_3$)	Sphingosine	pK in region of pH 7·5
Phosphate-choline (PO_4^-, $-\overset{+}{N}Me$)	Lecithin Sphingomyelin Lysolecithin	Isoelectric over wide pH range 3·5–10
Phosphate-amine (PO_4^-, $-\overset{+}{N}H_3$)	Phosphatidyl-ethanolamine	Net negative at pH 7·5
Phosphate-amine-carboxyl (PO_4^-, $\overset{+}{N}H_3$, COO^-)	Phosphatidylserine	Net negative at pH 7·5

as PO_4^-, N^+H_3, and COO^- in phospholipids such as the phosphatidylserines is important because of their ability to chelate ions of metals such as calcium and magnesium.

The electrostatic field at the interface between the phospholipid and the bulk aqueous phase is an important property. As we have seen, phospholipid molecules at interfaces orientate themselves in such a way that their ionic portion (head group) is directed towards the aqueous phase and their hydrophobic fatty acid chains towards the interior of the particle. The electrostatic charges on the head groups attract oppositely charged counter ions in the bulk aqueous phase. The distribution of these counter ions determines the potential gradient from the plane of the head groups into the aqueous phase; the total potential difference is known as the ψ-potential. Some of the counter ions will travel with the particle when it moves in an applied electrical field. The potential (relative to that of the bulk aqueous phase) at the plane of shear between the particle with its associated counter ions and the bulk phase is known as the ζ-potential. It can be calculated from the rate of movement of the particle in the applied electrical field and is a measure of the surface-charge density. See Fig. 4.21.

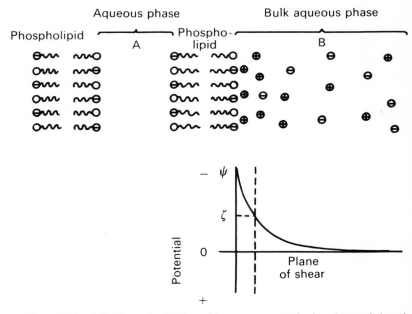

Fig. 4.21. *(a) Phospholipids with some negatively charged head groups in a bilayer arrangement in water. (b) The ψ and ζ-potentials which can affect the rate of phospholipase attack on lecithin*

The potential gradient at the phospholipid-water interface can play a major part in determining (a) the packing and alignment of adjacent phospholipid molecules in the interface, and whether dispersion of the laminated form into spherical micelles or transitional states takes place, and (b) the approach and orientation of an attacking enzyme molecule. These factors can, of course, have a pronounced influence on the rate of enzyme action. The effective charge at the interface can be varied by mixing compounds with amphipathic anions or cations with the phospholipid or by adding suitable water-soluble counter ions to the aqueous medium to mask the effect of the surface charge.

Experimental model membrane systems

Despite our present uncertainty of the details of biological membrane structure and the doubts which some scientists have as to whether the main structural unit of biological membranes really does consist predominantly of phospholipid bilayers, model systems have recently been created which consist of individual phospholipid bilayers or, alternatively, consist of a concentric arrangement of phospholipid bilayers. An important advance was made in 1962 when Mueller and co-workers reported that, after painting phospholipid across an orifice, the bulk lipid drains and thins from a thick film which is coloured in white light to a black stable phospholipid film some 10 mm square in area separating a 0·1 M solution (see Fig. 4.22). The black film is considered to be bimolecular and could be made to support two aqueous compartments. The dimensions of the bilayer were estimated on the basis of optical and electrical capacity studies to be between 60 and 90 Å thick.

When protein obtained from various biological sources is added to these bilayers a drop in resistance occurs from 10^8 to about

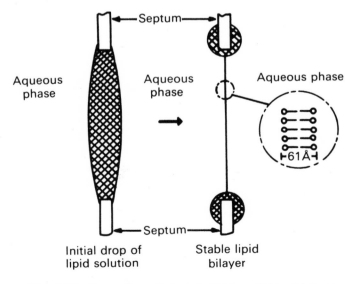

Fig. 4.22. *Formation of phospholipid model membranes*

10^3–10^5 ohm/cm^2. What has made this work particularly provoca-tive and exciting was the fact that this made the films active or electrically excitable, i.e., their resistance changes reversibly and regeneratively between two values in response to a suprathreshold applied voltage. The exciting feature of this work is that the total kinetics of the resistance system is similar to that of the action potential of frog nerve in 0·1 M KCl. The lipid used in these experi-ments was extracted from white matter of brain. With the addition of a substance such as tetradecane, squalene, caprylic acid, and α-toco-pherol, films were formed which were stable for at least 24 hours.

In the last three or four years many studies have been made on these systems. Some workers have suggested that there is a tempera-ture dependence of the bilayer specific resistance and other workers have considered the organization and orientation of the lipids within the bilayer, and concluded that the phosphate and trimethylam-monium groups of the lecithin molecules are in a plane parallel to the bilayer.

Recently, amongst the biological materials added to these black films have been antibiotics such as valinomycin, actin, and enniatin. The adsorption of these molecules increases the membrane con-ductance up to 10^3 times. The single ionic conductances are observed to differ by as much as 300 times and, interestingly, have been found to show discrimination between sodium and potassium ions. A resting potential of up to 150 mV is given when 0·1 M solutions of sodium chloride and potassium chloride are placed on opposite sides of the bilayer. This is also a property similar to that obtained with natural biological membranes. These bilayer films have also been used to simulate antibody reactions.

In an alternative model system, Bangham and co-workers have used phospholipid globules or dispersions in water to provide an experimental model system for the study of ion permeability. The system consists essentially of a dispersed phospholipid, such as lecithin, which contains up to 15 per cent dicetylphosphoric acid and, in some cases, phosphatidic acid. The lecithin is known to form lamellar structures of phospholipid bilayers separated by aqueous compartments (see Fig. 4.21). The presence of phosphatidic acid, or dicetyl phosphoric acid, gives a net charge to the lipid and causes a separation of the adjacent layers. If the phospholipid is allowed to swell in the presence of ions, the ions can be trapped in aqueous layers. Diffusions of the ions through the bilayers can then be studied.

Recent studies have shown that, as the negative charge on the structure decreases, so does the diffusion rate for cations leaving the phospholipid. Anions, however, are found to diffuse much more rapidly than cations and appear to be relatively free to diffuse whether fixed charges of either sign are present or not. These globules have also been shown to have osmotic properties similar to those of cell membranes. They are also considered to exhibit other properties which simulate the properties of natural membrane systems, e.g., ion transport through these globules is affected by steroids in a similar way to the effect of steroids on natural membranes.

Monolayer studies

A number of monolayer studies at the air–water interface have been made with phospholipids of various types. The films obtained with phospholipids containing fully saturated chains (e.g., distearoyl-phosphatidylethanolamine) are condensed in character. As the chain length of the fatty acid residue decreases, or as the amount of *cis* unsaturation increases, the films become more expanded. The type of film observed parallels the temperature at which the transition from crystalline to liquid crystalline occurs, i.e., at room temperature a condensed film is observed with those phospholipids which have a high transition temperature, and an expanded film with phospholipids which have a transition temperature close to or lower than room temperature. The type of monolayer obtained appears to be a reflection of the degree of twisting and flexing of the hydrocarbon chains. Thus most natural phospholipids give expanded monomolecular films and the chains are in a very mobile condition at room temperature. Only very small differences are observed between positional isomers so that similar films are observed whether the unsaturated chain is in the 1 or 2-position. Divalent cations (Ca^{2+}) have been shown to produce a small condensation effect on monolayers of phosphatidylserine.

Mixed films of phospholipids with cholesterol show that these phospholipids which give an expanded film undergo condensation when cholesterol is present, i.e., the space taken by the phospholipid is *less* with cholesterol than when it is absent. This condensing effect is observed with saturated phospholipids if the temperature is raised. This effect is not observed with either lecithins or phosphatidylethanolamines containing linoleic or linolenic acid residues.

Biological Relevance

It is well known that phospholipids cannot be extracted from animal tissues with diethyl ether if a preliminary treatment with a polar solvent, such as ethanol, is omitted. Such treatment is necessary to release phospholipids from the native complexed forms, e.g., lipoproteins, in which they occur in most tissues. Accordingly, free phospholipids isolated from solvent extracts of tissues are largely regarded as artefacts. For many years phospholipid molecules have been recognized as important components of natural cell membranes. Korn has recently summarized the phosphoglyceride composition of a number of animal and bacterial membranes. This is shown in Table 4.3. As early as 1930 it was suggested that the structure of the natural membrane consists essentially of a phospholipid bilayer sandwiched between globular protein. There appears to be good evidence from X-ray diffraction studies that a lamellar type of organization occurs in the nerve myelin sheath, although it is not found in all membrane systems. In fact, it is believed that a wide range and variety of lipoprotein structure occurs in various membranes. Such complexes may be formed, in principle, either by interactions involving the polar groups of the phospholipids (Coulombic

Table 4.3. Phosphoglyceride composition of animal and bacterial membranes
(E. D. Korn, *Science*, **153**, 1491, 1966)

	Myelin	Erythro-cyte	Mito-chondria	Micro-some	Azoto-bacter agilis	Escheri-chia coli
Cholesterol	25	25	5	6	0	0
Phosphatidyl-ethanolamine	14	20	28	17	100	100
Phosphatidylserine	7	11	0	0	0	0
Phosphatidylcholine	11	23	48	64	0	0
Phosphatidylinositol	0	2	8	11	0	0
Phosphatidylglycerol	0	0	1	2	0	0
Cardiolipin	0	0	11	0	0	0
Sphingomyelin	6	18	0	0	0	0
Cerebroside	21	0	0	0	0	0
Cerebroside sulphate	4	0	0	0	0	0
Ceramide	1	0	0	0	0	0
Lysylphosphatidyl glycerol	0	0	0	0	0	0
Unknown or other	12	2	0	0	0	0

and/or hydrogen bonding) or through their fatty chains (hydrophobic interaction), and perhaps both may be involved together in a dynamic situation. For example, the hydrophobic bonding has been suggested to occur in the chloroplast and also in the mitochondrial membrane. This is shown schematically in Fig. 7.1 wherein the hydrocarbon chains of the lipid are shown situated within the protein system.

The need for several phosphoglycerides in membrane organization is understood only vaguely, or not at all at present. It is significant that, in the membranes in most animal tissues, more than 50 per cent of the total phospholipid present may contain choline. However, the relative amounts of phosphoglyceride and sphingophospholipid can differ considerably even in the same membrane type from different animals.

The choline-containing phosphoglycerides are perhaps preferred because they have a net zero charge at physiological pH. However, in some membranes (bacterial), a predominance of negatively charged phospholipids does occur. The particular charge distribution set up for the phosphoglycerides in a membrane may be important for determining specific interactions with proteins.

Another possibility is that the different classes are present so as to produce the correct liquid crystalline phase organization, say lamellar or hexagonal, at a particular temperature for certain membrane interactions or functions to occur. Studies of the clot-accelerating property of phospholipids have shown that it is directly related to the sign and magnitude of the surface charge on the lipids. The activity of some of the phospholipase enzymes has also been shown to be strongly affected by surface charge requirements.

Some of the polar groups of the phosphoglycerides can interact strongly with metal ions and it has been speculated that phosphatidylserine in a membrane will interact with Ca^{2+} or Mg^{2+} ions and adopt in water a particular liquid crystalline configuration. It has been suggested that competition for the metal ions between ATP near the membrane and the phospholipid may modify this organization and that this could be relevant to membrane processes.

Certain polar groupings may be concerned with ion transport processes. It is known that the concentration of sodium ions is lower and potassium ions is higher inside the cell than in the surrounding fluid, and that concentrations are regulated by the cell membrane. Participation by phosphatidylserine, phosphatidic acids and phosphatidylcholines has been invoked in the molecular mechanism underlying this process.

Phosphatidylserine is known to take up potassium ions in preference to sodium ions from aqueous systems. Phosphatidic acid has been suggested to be a carrier molecule for sodium ions. It is said to be synthesized from ATP and diglyceride at the inner surface of a membrane and to act as an ATPase. Another theory suggests that lecithin is hydrolysed by a phospholipase D to choline and phosphatidic acid at the inner membrane and then the phosphatidic acid transports sodium ions. None of these ion transport theories has yet received acceptance and some scientists consider that the phospholipid merely provides a useful matrix for organizing the enzyme systems involved in the transport processes.

Little is yet known about the biosynthesis and turnover of the amino acid esters. It has been suggested that the identification of some lipoamino acids as esters of phosphatidylglycerol, which is metabolically active, offers support for the idea that they may play some part in transport and, directly or indirectly, in the synthesis of protein. However, they have not been identified in animal tissues, and the amino acids so far identified as constituents of such esters, far from comprising a representative range required for protein synthesis, are very limited in number, usually only one in each species of bacteria, and lysine, ornithine, or alanine are apparently selectively incorporated, though small amounts of other amino acids have been found. In *Micrococcus lysodeikticus* the phospholipid fraction, which is mainly phosphatidylglycerol, contained no amino acids, even in metabolizing cultures. The formation of these amino acid esters is therefore not a general phenomenon, even in gram-positive bacteria.

When we consider the variety of fatty acids associated with the phosphoglycerides ranging in chain length, branching, and unsaturation, there are a few generalizations which seem pertinent.

(a) It seems reasonable to suggest that the reason why the chains are usually fairly long is probably to enable the lipid to have the correct hydrophobic/hydrophilic balance for membrane organization, e.g., short chains would make the lipid too water-soluble.

(b) If we recall that a decrease in chain length, or an increase in branching or unsaturation can lead to a reduction of the dispersion forces between the chains, we see another possible generalization. It seems reasonable that a particular membrane has to have a certain optimum fluidity in order to carry out its various functions, e.g., this might be to allow diffusion or metabolic processes to occur, say at body temperature. The required fluidity for a given phospholipid can, in principle, be obtained either by shortening the chain or varying the amount of unsaturation or introduction of branching. The great importance of proper fluidity of fatty chains is brought out strikingly in experiments with yeast cells. During normal (aerobic) growth, the cells synthesize phospholipids containing long-chain unsaturated fatty acyl residue in the 2-position of glycerol. When the cells were grown anaerobically, medium/short chain saturated fatty acids were incorporated in place of the long-chain unsaturated residues. Under anaerobic conditions, the oxidative mechanisms for production of unsaturation are not available and it seems as though the organism makes an attempt to retain the same fluidity as it possessed when synthesis occurred under aerobic conditions. Other studies on poikilothermic organisms and bacteria appear to show similar effects, e.g., plants, insects, goldfish, and bacteria reared under lower than normal temperatures show increasing unsaturation in the phospholipids.

There may be other reasons for the presence of individual acids or particular types of fatty acid distribution. The variation in fatty acid content and polar groups may be interrelated. It is usually ignored that the transition temperature of a given fatty acid in phosphoglycerides varies with the class of phosphoglyceride with which it is associated.

Cholesterol is found in many cell membranes but the reason for its presence is not understood. It may control in a reversible way the fluidity of the membrane. It has been suggested that cholesterol distinguishes the eucaryotic from the procaryotic type membranes. Polyene antibiotics have been shown to be effective agents against those cells which contain sterols in their membranes. Bacteria and blue-green algae, both organisms which are sterol-less, resist the effect of these antibiotics.

Many of the enzyme complexes of the electron transport chains in mitochondria can be isolated as discrete lipoproteins and phospholipids are thought to be involved in the electron transport system. Removal of phospholipid from these lipoproteins causes a loss of enzyme activity. The addition of purified phospholipids and ubiquinone restores the activity. It has been shown that the reduction of cytochrome C by reduced ubiquinone and the reduction of oxygen by reduced cytochrome C are all reactivated by the addition of phospholipid to lipid-depleted mitochondria. The degree of reactivation in each case is proportional to the amount of phospholipid bound to the mitochondria.

The reason why phospholipids are essential components of such enzyme complexes is not known precisely. They are said to act as cement substances holding the individual enzymes with their active centres oriented towards one another so as to ensure maximal activity, or alternatively, to provide a medium for electron flow within complexes and between complexes. Thus in mitochondria the function of the phospholipid appears to be mainly non-specific in the sense that restoration of the enzymic activity can be brought about by a variety of individual phospholipids. Phospholipids are considered to be intimately involved in enzyme reactions leading to the biosynthesis of macromolecular components of bacterial cell envelope molecules such as lipopolysaccharides.

Phospholipids are also important in plasma lipoproteins although their precise function here is, as yet, unknown. The apoprotein from the α-lipoprotein has, however, been shown to combine with phospholipids in the absence of a coupled energy source to form a complex having definite physicochemical and functional properties. Studies are being made of this complex in order to try to throw light on to the nature of the lipid-protein association involved.

Other functions of phospholipids, such as their use as energy-providing substrates, seem to be of comparatively minor significance. During cell division increased synthesis of phospholipid occurs; presumably the new phospholipid is required for the formation of the additional membrane structure in each daughter cell. It has been suggested that exchange of phospholipid molecules may be an intrinsic and necessary characteristic of membrane systems so as to allow them to expand, contract, and convolute during cellular activity.

Because phosphoglycerides are components of cell membranes, speculations link them to a range of cell behaviour. Thus they have been implicated in (a) the organization of energy transfer molecules such as chlorophyll and β-carotene, (b) anaesthetic, olfactory, and drug action as well as other effects relating to triggering membranes, (c) the nerve impulse mechanism, (d) a part in protein synthesis, (e) some rôle in cell adhesiveness and cancer, (f) some connection with atherosclerosis (the first signs of atheroma are fatty streaks which contain phospholipid, triglyceride, and cholesterol) either through some metabolic process or through its connection with blood coagulation.

Further reading

General

G. B. Ansell and J. N. Hawthorne, *Phospholipids*. Elsevier, 1964.
L. L. M. van Deenen, *Phospholipids and Biomembranes*. Pergamon Press, 1965.

Synthesis

E. Baer, *Can. J. Biochem. Physiol.*, **34**, 288 (1956).
L. L. M. van Deenen and G. H. de Haas, *Advances in Lipid Research*, Vol. 2, p. 167, Academic Press, 1964.
T. Malkin, *Chem. & Ind.*, 605 (1961).
T. Malkin and T. H. Bevan, *Progress in Chemistry of Fats and Other Lipids*, Vol. 4, 97 (1957).

Structure and Analysis

G. Rouser, G. Kritchevsky, C. Galli, and D. Heller, *J. Am. Oil Chem. Soc.*, **42**, 215 (1965).
C. E. Ballou and Y. C. Lee, *Cyclitols and Phosphoinositides*, Vol. 2, Pergamon Press (1966).
E. D. Korn, *Science*, **153**, 1491 (1966).

Metabolism and Serum Lipoproteins

R. M. C. Dawson, *Essays in Biochemistry*, Vol. 2, p. 69. Academic Press, 1966.
A. Scanu, *J. Biol. Chem.*, **242**, 711 (1967).

Physical Properties

A. D. Bangham, *Advances in Lipid Research*, **1**, 65 (1963).
D. Chapman, P. Byrne, and G. G. Shipley, *Proc. Roy. Soc. A*, **290**, 115 (1966).
D. G. Dervichian, *Progress in Biophysics and Molecular Biology*, **14**, 265 (1964).
J. B. Finean, *Progress in Biophysics and Molecular Biology*, **16**, 143 (1966).
J. L. Kavanau, *Structure and Function in Biological Membranes*. Holden-Day, Vol. 1, 1965.
P. Mueller, D. O. Rudin, H. Ti Tien, and W. C. Wescott, *Recent Progress in Surface Science*, p. 379, Academic Press, 1964.

5. Sphingolipids

Structure and Occurrence

Sphingolipids are defined as those lipids which contain the long-chain amino-alcohol sphingosine. These lipids are analogous to the lipids derived from glycerol but instead sphingosine is the characteristic polyalcohol.

There are various sub-classes of sphingolipids. These include sphingomyelin, cerebrosides, sulphates, ceramide-polyhexosides and gangliosides.

The content of some sphingosine lipids in various membranes are shown in Table 4.1 given in chapter 4. These sphingolipids often accumulate in various organs in certain metabolic lipid disorders (lipidoses). Attempts to understand the chemistry and causes of the variations in these disease states have stimulated investigations. Another impetus for these studies has been increased emphasis on experimentation aimed towards an understanding of brain chemistry, metabolism, and function.

Sphingosine

The structure of sphingosine is shown. It has been identified both by degradation methods and by synthesis and shown to be D-erythro-1,3-dihydroxy-2-amino-4-*trans*-octadecene

$$CH(OH)CH=CH(CH_2)_{12}CH_3$$
$$CHNH_2$$
$$CH_2OH$$

Sphingosine

Recently it has been shown that sphingosine is only one of a homologous series of compounds. Sphingosine itself contains 18 carbon atoms and is sometimes indicated 18:sphingosine. The related compounds are 20:sphingosine which is D-erythro-1,3-dihydroxy-2-amino-4-*trans*-eicosene; dihydrosphingosine (18:dihydrosphingosine) which is D-erythro-1,3-dihydroxy-2-amino-octadecane; 20:dihydrosphingosine which is D-erythro-1,3-dihydroxy-2-amino-eicosane; phytosphingosine (18:phytosphingosine) which is D-erythro-1,3,4-trihydroxy-2-amino-octadecane; 20:phytosphingosine which is D-erythro-1,3,4-trihydroxy-2-amino-eicosane.

Sphingosine can combine with fatty acids, phosphorus, and bases to form the sphingomyelins. The structure of sphingomyelin is shown:

CH(OH)CH=CH(CH$_2$)$_{12}$CH$_3$ where R is a fatty alkyl group

CHNHOCR

$$CH_2OPOCH_2CH_2\overset{+}{N}(CH_3)_3$$
O
‖
O$^-$. (H, OH)

Sphingomyelin

The similarity of the structure of sphingomyelin and the phosphatidylcholines (see chapter 4) is apparent. On carbon 1 is substituted the phosphorylcholine group, whilst carbon 2 has attached a long-chain fatty acid and carbon 3 has attached a hydrocarbon residue. Long-chain saturated fatty acids, predominantly stearic, lignoceric ($C_{23}H_{47}CO_2H$), and nervonic acids have been isolated from naturally occurring sphingomyelin. The structure and configuration of sphingomyelin have been established by synthesis.

The fatty acids found are more saturated than those observed with the phosphoglycerides. The typical predominant acid is lignoceric acid. The sphingomyelin from brain is associated with stearic and nervonic acids as well as lignoceric acid. (Nervonic acid is tetracos-15-enoic acid.) The sphingomyelin from lung contains equal proportions of palmitic and lignoceric acids.

Ceramides and cerebrosides

The fatty acid amides of the sphingosines are known. These are called the ceramides. The structure of a ceramide is shown:

$$CH(OH)CH{=}CH(CH_2)_{12}CH_3$$
$$CHNHOCR$$
$$CH_2{-}OH \qquad\qquad R = \text{long-chain alkyl}$$
$$\text{group}$$

Ceramide

Cerebrosides contain either sphingosine or dihydrosphingosine, a long-chain fatty acid, and a sugar. They are similar to the sphingomyelins except that, instead of the phosphorylcholine group, they contain a sugar. The sugar is either glucose or galactose in a β-glycosidic linkage on the terminal carbon of the sphingosine. The term is used generally for ceramide-monohexosides. In the past cerebrosides have been variously designated as galactolipids, glycolipids, and glycosphingosides.

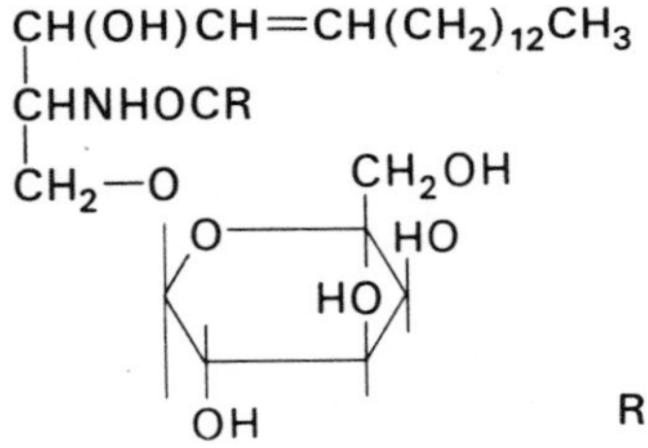

$$CH(OH)CH{=}CH(CH_2)_{12}CH_3$$
$$CHNHOCR$$
$$CH_2{-}O \qquad CH_2OH$$

R = alkyl group

Cerebroside

Four different types of fatty acids give rise to four different types of cerebrosides. These are cerasin, phrenosin (cerebron), nervon, and oxynervon. The acyl group in cerasin corresponds to lignoceric acid. In phrenosin the acyl group is mainly cerebronic acid (an α-hydroxy saturated acid). In nervon the acyl group is the mono-unsaturated acid, nervonic acid.

Alkaline hydrolysis of the peptide bond of cerebroside produces the molecule psychosine whose structure is shown:

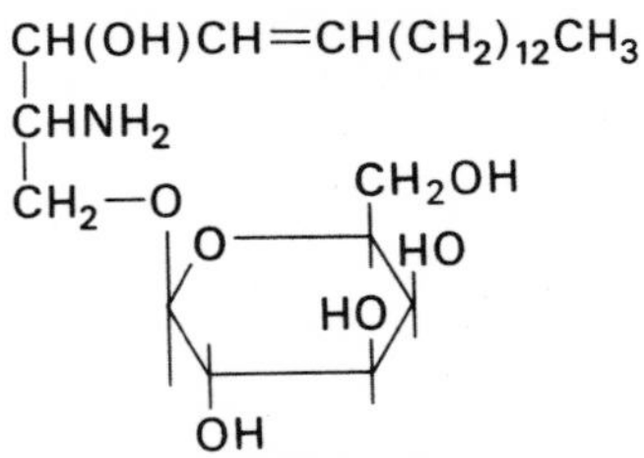

$$CH(OH)CH{=}CH(CH_2)_{12}CH_3$$
$$CHNH_2$$
$$CH_2{-}O \qquad CH_2OH$$

Psychosine

In brain tissue the cerebrosides are partly present as sulphatides. One cerebroside molecule contains one molecule of sulphuric acid. The linkage is through the hydroxyl group on carbon atom 3 of the galactose ring.

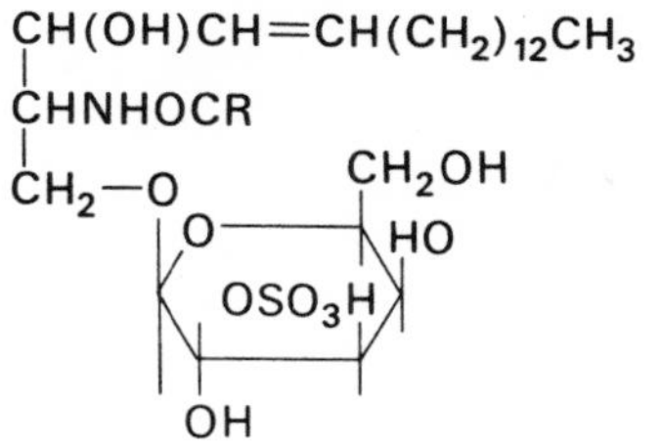

$$CH(OH)CH=CH(CH_2)_{12}CH_3$$
$$CHNHOCR$$
$$CH_2-O$$

CH₂OH / HO / O / OSO₃H / OH

A sulphatide

Other molecules similar to cerebrosides, but containing two sugar groups and others with three and also four sugar groups, have been observed. The cerebrosides with more than one hexose are called ceramide-polyhexosides. The dihexoside has been found in the kidneys of patients with Fabry's disease. An O'-disaccharide of N-acyl sphingosine (a ceramide lactose) is found in normal ox

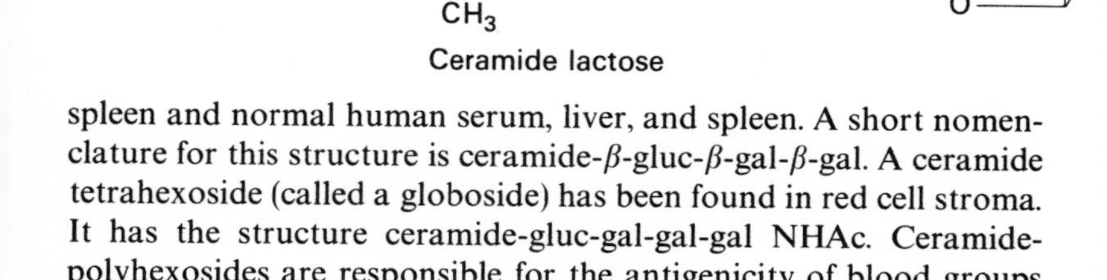

$$H_3-(CH_2)_{12}-CH=CH-CH-CH-CH_2-O$$

OH NH / C=O / $(CH_2)_{16-22}$ / CH₃ / OH / HOCH₂ / O / OH / HOCH₂ / O

Ceramide lactose

spleen and normal human serum, liver, and spleen. A short nomenclature for this structure is ceramide-β-gluc-β-gal-β-gal. A ceramide tetrahexoside (called a globoside) has been found in red cell stroma. It has the structure ceramide-gluc-gal-gal-gal NHAc. Ceramide-polyhexosides are responsible for the antigenicity of blood groups A and B.

Gangliosides

The name ganglioside originated from studies of the ganglion cells of the nervous system. Among the hydrolysis products are fatty acids, sphingosine, galactose, and glucose. Most gangliosides also contain hexosamine. They differ from the cerebrosides in giving an additional important product on hydrolysis. This additional component is called sialic acid. The sialic acids are acylated neuraminic acids and sialic acid is a group name. They can be considered to be the product of an aldol condensation between N-acylmannosamine and pyruvic acid. All naturally occurring sialic acids are N-acylated. Some of them are additionally O-substituted.

In brain gangliosides the presence of only N-acetylneuraminic acid (NANA) has been *indicated*. At least ten different gangliosides have been isolated from brain. Four of these are major components. The four major gangliosides isolated from human or beef brain have a common basic structure. This is galactosyl-N-acetylgalacto-saminyl-galactosyl-glucosyl ceramide to which is bound one to three molecules of sialic acid. The formulae for a number of gangliosides using a short-hand nomenclature are given in Table 5.1.

Table 5.1. Ganglioside convention

A_1	cer ← 1gal(3 ← 2)NANA
B_1	cer ← 1glu(4 ← 1)gal(3 ← 2)NANA
B_2	cer ← 1glu(4 ← 1)gal [(3 ← 2)NANA](4 ← 1)galNAc
B_3	cer ← 1glu(4 ← 1)gal [(3 ← 2)NANA](4 ← 1)galNAc (3 ← 1)gal
B_4	cer ← 1glu(4 ← 1)gal[(3 ← 2)NANA](4 ← 1)galNAc (3 ← 1)gal(3 ← 2)NANA
C_1	cer ← 1glu(4 ← 1)gal(3 ← 2)NANA(8 ← 2)NANA
C_2	cer ← 1glu(4 ← 1)gal [(3 ← 2)NANA(8 ← 2)NANA] (4 ← 1)galNAc
C_3	cer ← 1glu(4 ← 1)gal [(3 ← 2)NANA(8 ← 2)NANA] (4 ← 1)galNAc(3 ← 1)gal

The full structure of ganglioside B_3 is shown in Fig. 5.1.

Four other minor gangliosides have been detected in normal human brain. In Tay–Sachs disease one of the gangliosides (B_2), which is normally present at a level of only 3 to 6 per cent, constitutes more than 90 per cent of the total gangliosides.

The major fatty acid of brain gangliosides is stearic acid. It constitutes 80–90 per cent of the total fatty acids of brain gangliosides of mammals and also other vertebrates. In horse erythrocyte, lignoceric acid is the major fatty acid, whilst in dog erythrocytes, nervonic acid is also present in large amounts.

The major long chain bases of brain gangliosides are C_{18}-sphingosine and C_{20}-sphingosine.

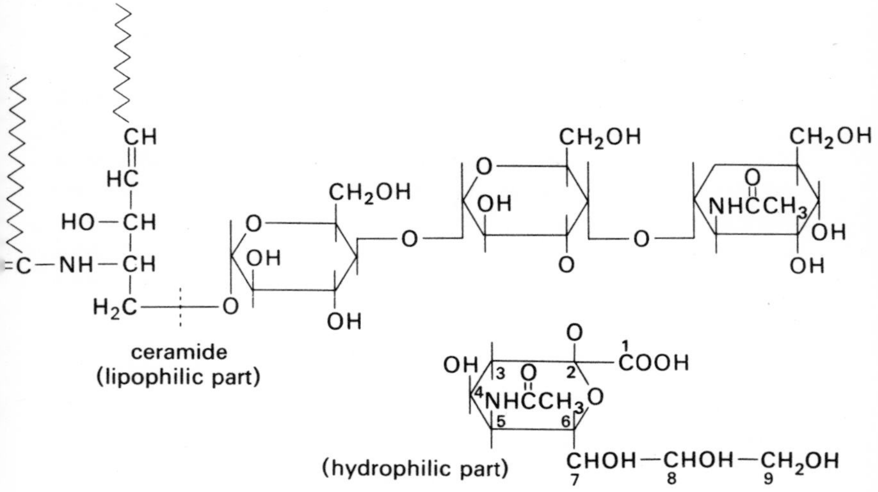

Fig. 5.1. *The structure of a ganglioside* (B_3)

Analysis

Sphingosine

Sphingosine is usually isolated by hydrolysis of sphingolipids with N sulphuric acid in methanol under reflux for a number of hours. Alternatively 2N HCl in methanol can be used. After removal of fatty acids with petroleum ether, the aqueous methanolic solution is neutralized and the crude base fraction is extracted with ether. The ether is then removed, the residue dissolved in ethanol, and the sphingosine bases precipitated with sulphuric acid to give sphingosine and dihydrosphingosine sulphates.

Sphingomyelin

After extracting sterols and phosphoglycerides from natural tissues using acetone and dry ether, sphingolipids are extracted with hot alcohol. On cooling, a mixture of sphingomyelin and cerebroside is precipitated. The mixture may be partially separated by fractionation from glacial acetic acid or chloroform-methanol, in which sphingo-myelin is more soluble. The last trace of cerebroside is removed from the preparation by passing a solution in petroleum ether–methanol through an alumina column. The product in the eluate is recrystallized from ethyl acetate.

Analytical methods for estimating sphingomyelin in tissues depend on the assay for choline after total alkaline hydrolysis with barium hydroxide. A direct determination of sphingomyelin as an acetone-insoluble reineckate has been described. The usual tests for purity of sphingomyelin involve the determination of N/P ratios, analysis for the absence of carbohydrate, ester groups or glycerol, plasmalogen, and ninhydrin-reacting substances. Purified sphingo-myelins are white crystalline solids which are soluble in benzene, warm ethanol, and hot ethyl acetate, and are insoluble in ether and acetone.

Cerebrosides

The cerebrosides are insoluble in ether and soluble in hot alcohol. Purification of cerebrosides from crude, cold alcohol-insoluble lipid mixtures can be accomplished by crystallization from hot glacial acetic acid to give a preparation enriched in cerebrosides. This, however, contains phosphoglycerides.

Assays for cerebrosides are based on the sugar content after acid hydrolysis. Since lipids other than cerebrosides contain carbohy-drate, preliminary purification leads to more accurate analyses. Tests for purity also include determination of the absence of phos-phorus, ester groups, and ninhydrin-reacting substances. Cerebro-sides are white crystalline-appearing solids.

Gangliosides

Gangliosides are isolated, by dialysis against water, after extraction of the tissue lipids with chloroform–methanol 2:1, v/v. The ganglio-sides occur in the aqueous layer, whilst the other lipids stay in the chloroform layer. With this partition dialysis method, there is good recovery of the gangliosides, but the method allows preparation of only small amounts. The ganglioside mixture in the upper phase is also contaminated with polar lipids, such as sulphatides and phos-phatidylserine, and large amounts of non-lipid impurities that are very difficult to remove.

Another method gives a nearly quantitative recovery of ganglio-sides under mild conditions. In this method a total lipid extract is applied to a cellulose powder column and the bulk of lipids, other than gangliosides, are eluted with chloroform containing small amounts of alcohol and water. The gangliosides are retained on the column and can be eluted with alcohol- and water-enriched solvents. By this procedure a partial separation of the gangliosides into sialic acid-poor and sialic acid-rich fractions occurs. The method has lately been applied to the quantitative isolation of brain gangliosides.

Chromatography on silicic acid with chloroform–methanol mixtures has, in several instances, been found to be superior for the separation of gangliosides and their final purification.

Pure gangliosides can be obtained by a combination of modern chromatographic methods, but there is as yet no ideal method of separating all the individual gangliosides from one another.

Elemental analyses are of limited value, as large admixtures of, for example, other glycolipids, give only small deviations of the analytical results. Analyses of glucose, galactose, galactosamine, and sialic acid with reliable methods and standard substances are essential for the investigation of purity, homogeneity, and chemical structure of gangliosides.

Of the physicochemical methods, electrophoresis and ultra-centrifugal analysis are commonly used as tests of chemical homogeneity. A single moving boundary in these methods is, however, no proof for homogeneity.

Partition chromatography on thin-layers of silica gel is considered to be the best aid in the determination of purity and homogeneity of gangliosides. Before the introduction of thin-layer chromatography, partition chromatography on untreated or silica-impregnated papers was used with satisfactory results.

Chemical Synthesis

Sphingosine

A number of chemical syntheses for sphingosine and dihydro-sphingosine have been developed. The oxime of methyl-3-keto-octadecanoate (a) (Fig. 5.2) is reduced first with hydrogen over palladium or charcoal in the presence of hydrochloric acid to the amine hydrochloride (b), then with Adam's catalyst and hydrogen

to the hydroxy ester (c), and finally with lithium aluminium hydride
to dihydrosphingosine (d). The product is a mixture of racemates.

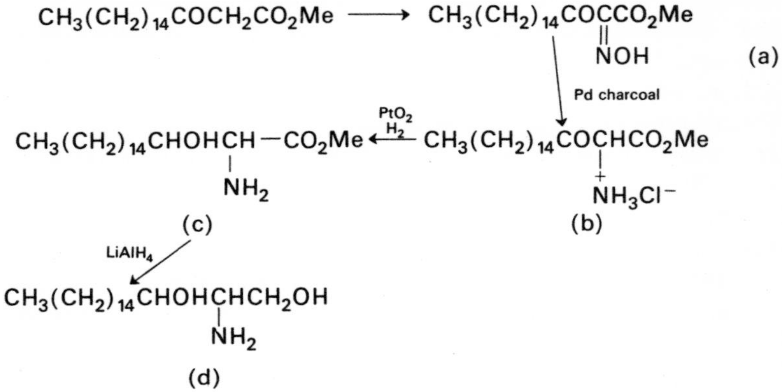

$$CH_3(CH_2)_{14}COCH_2CO_2Me \longrightarrow CH_3(CH_2)_{14}COCCO_2Me$$

$$\underset{NOH}{|} \qquad (a)$$

$$\xrightarrow{\text{Pd charcoal}}$$

$$CH_3(CH_2)_{14}CHOHCH-CO_2Me \xleftarrow[\text{H}_2]{\text{PtO}_2} CH_3(CH_2)_{14}COCHCO_2Me$$

$$\underset{NH_2}{|} \qquad \qquad \underset{\overset{+}{N}H_3Cl^-}{|}$$

$$\text{(c)} \qquad \qquad \text{(b)}$$

$$\downarrow \text{LiAlH}_4$$

$$CH_3(CH_2)_{14}CHOHCHCH_2OH$$

$$\underset{NH_2}{|}$$

$$\text{(d)}$$

Fig. 5.2. A synthesis of dihydrosphingosine

Dihydrosphingosine has been prepared by another route (Fig.
5.3). Ethyl palmitoyl acetoacetate (a) is coupled with benzene
diazonium chloride, and the product is reductively acetylated to an
amide (b) which is reduced with lithium aluminium hydride to
N-acetyl dihydrosphingosine (c). The pure *erythro* N-acetyl compound is obtained after recrystallization.

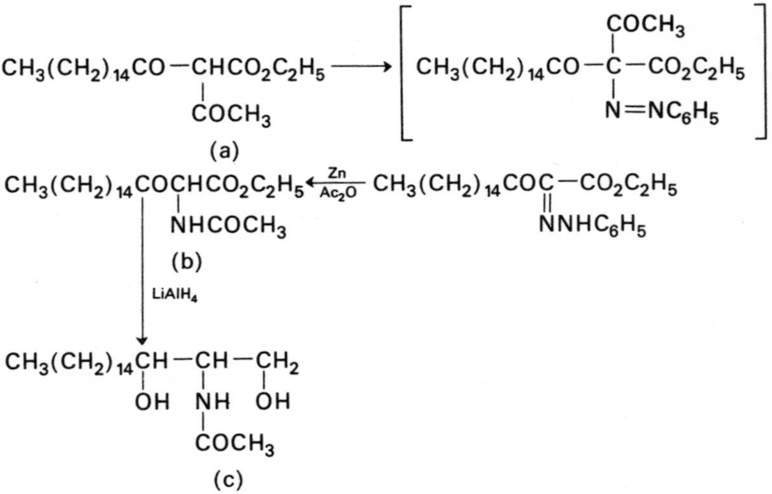

$$CH_3(CH_2)_{14}CO-CHCO_2C_2H_5 \longrightarrow \left[CH_3(CH_2)_{14}CO-\underset{\overset{|}{N=NC_6H_5}}{\overset{\overset{COCH_3}{|}}{C}}-CO_2C_2H_5 \right]$$

$$\underset{COCH_3}{|}$$

$$\text{(a)}$$

$$CH_3(CH_2)_{14}COCHCO_2C_2H_5 \xleftarrow{\frac{Zn}{Ac_2O}} CH_3(CH_2)_{14}COC-CO_2C_2H_5$$

$$\underset{NHCOCH_3}{|} \qquad \qquad \underset{NNHC_6H_5}{\|}$$

$$\text{(b)}$$

$$\downarrow \text{LiAlH}_4$$

$$CH_3(CH_2)_{14}CH-CH-CH_2$$

$$\underset{OH}{|} \quad \underset{NH}{|} \quad \underset{OH}{|}$$

$$\underset{COCH_3}{|}$$

$$\text{(c)}$$

Fig. 5.3. A synthesis of dihydrosphingosine

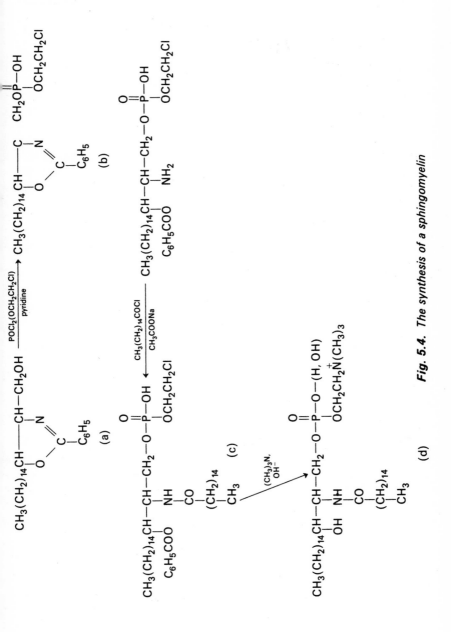

Fig. 5.4. The synthesis of a sphingomyelin

A similar series of reactions has been used for the preparation of DL-*erythro* sphingosine.

Sphingomyelin

The synthesis of dihydrosphingomyelin has recently been described and is shown in Fig. 5.4. The key intermediate in the preparation is a hydroxymethyl oxazoline (a) in which both the secondary hydroxyl and the amino group are blocked. This compound is treated with β-chloroethylphosphoryl dichloride in the presence of pyridine to yield the phosphate ester (b). After heating with hydrochloric acid to open the oxazoline ring, acylation with palmitoyl chloride in the presence of sodium acetate gives the amide. This is then treated with trimethylamine and subjected to mild alkaline hydrolysis to obtain palmitoyldihydrosphingomyelin (d).

Cerebroside

The synthesis of a dihydrocerebroside has been reported. The reaction sequence used is:

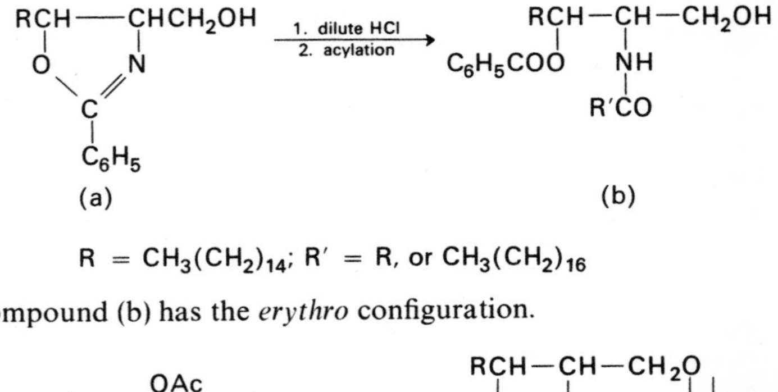

$$R = CH_3(CH_2)_{14}; \; R' = R, \text{ or } CH_3(CH_2)_{16}$$

Compound (b) has the *erythro* configuration.

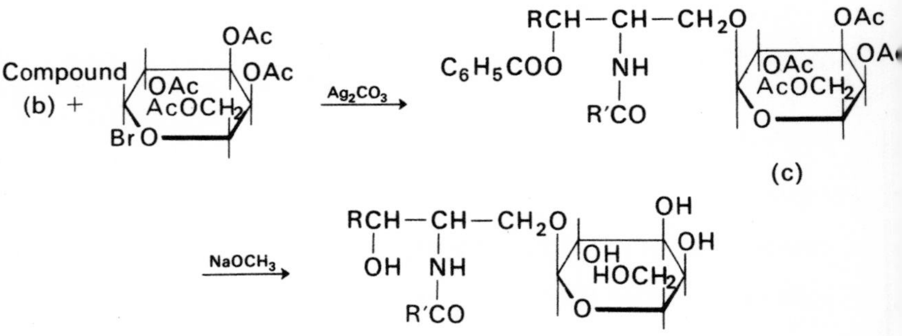

Fig. 5.5. The synthesis of a cerebroside

Biosynthesis

Sphingosine

The biosynthesis of sphingosine appears to occur by an aldol condensation of the Knoevenagel type between palmitic aldehyde and the activated (carbanion) methylene carbon of serine.

$$CH_2OHC^-(CO_2H)N:\text{pyridoxal phosphate} + CH_3[CH_2]_{14}CHO \xrightarrow{Mn^{2+}}$$

$$CH_3[CH_2]_{14}CH(OH)CH(NH_2)CH_2OH + CO_2 + \text{pyridoxal phosphate}$$

This activation occurs through the formation of a Schiff base-metal chelate between serine, pyridoxal phosphate, and Mn^{2+}. The product of the condensation is dihydrosphingosine, which is subsequently desaturated to form sphingosine.

$$CH_3[CH_2]_{12}CH_2CH_2CH(OH)CH(NH_2)CH_2OH + \text{flavin} \longrightarrow$$

$$CH_3[CH_2]_{12}CH{=}CHCH(OH)CH(NH_2)CH_2OH + \text{flavin 2H}$$

Cerebroside

Microsomal preparations obtained from young rat brain tissue contain enzymes which catalyse a number of reactions which ultimately lead to the incorporation of radioactivity from either labelled glucose or galactose into brain cerebrosides. The predominant product of this system is galactose cerebroside. The reactions are believed to occur according to the following schemes:

For glucose:

$$\text{glucose} + ATP \xrightarrow[\substack{\text{hexokinase}\\ \text{phosphoglucomutase}}]{Mg^{2+}} \text{glucose-1-PO}_4 + ADP$$

$$\text{glucose-1-PO}_4 + UTP \underset{\text{UDPG pyrophosphorylase}}{\rightleftharpoons} \text{UDP-glucose} + \text{pyrophosphate}$$

$$\text{UDP-glucose} \underset{\text{UDP galactose 4-epimerase}}{\rightleftharpoons} \text{UDP-galactose}$$

For galactose:

$$\text{galactose} + ATP \xrightarrow[\text{galactokinase}]{Mg^{2+}} \text{galactose-1-PO}_4 + ADP$$

$$\text{galactose-1-PO}_4 + \text{UDP-glucose} \underset{\substack{\text{galactose-1-PO}_4\\ \text{uridyl-transferase}}}{\rightleftharpoons}$$

$$\text{UDP-galactose} + \text{glucose-1-PO}_4$$

Studies with washed rat brain microsomes indicate that these particles contain enzymes which catalyse the total synthesis of cerebrosides from sphingosine, stearyl-CoA, and UDP-galactose or UDP-glucose. When exogenous sphingosine is added to the

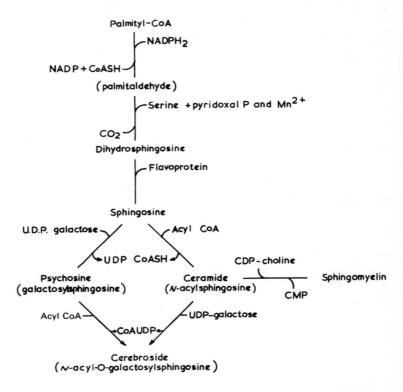

Fig. 5.6. *Inter-relationships which exist among the sphingolipids*

incubation system, the amount of labelled galactose incorporated into glycolipid is markedly increased.

Using labelled stearyl-CoA, the synthesis of cerebrosides is moderately stimulated by the inclusion of sphingosine and UDP-glucose in the incubation medium which probably are precursors of psychosine. The inclusion of ATP in the incubation medium also produces a marked increase in cerebroside synthesis in the presence of psychosine.

More work is required on the biosynthesis of these complex lipids, particularly the cerebrosides, sulphatides and gangliosides. The present known inter-relationships which exist among the sphingolipids are shown in Fig. 5.6.

Physical Properties

The sphingolipids, such as the sphingomyelins, have similar properties to the lecithins. They have high capillary melting points (near 210°C) but undergo thermal transitions at lower temperatures. In the presence of water the sphingomyelins exist in a lamellar phase. The cerebrosides in water also form a lamellar phase.

Some physical studies have been made with ganglioside molecules. These studies suggest that the gangliosides in water can form micelles and that the critical micelle concentration is low and is about 1.0×10^{-5} M. It is thought that there are about 100 molecules in each micelle.

Drying from aqueous solution leaves birefringent strands and electron microscopy shows layers 60 Å in thickness consisting of asymmetric particles. Gangliosides also form associations with dye molecules such as toluidine blue or pinacyanol to give different colours from that given by the dye itself. Only the more acidic gangliosides show this interaction.

Monomolecular films

A few monolayer studies have been made with sphingosine-containing lipids. Fractions of sphingomyelin from ox brain, containing a predominance of stearic acid on the one hand and nervonic acid on the other, have been examined at an air–water interface. The fraction containing stearic acid gives a condensed film, whilst the fraction containing nervonic acid gives an expanded film. The properties depend more upon whether the fatty acid is saturated or unsaturated rather than upon the type of base. Cerebrosides and sulphatides from ox brain have also been observed to give condensed films at pressures above 20 dyn/cm. Gangliosides, on the other hand, give highly expanded films. Ultrasonic irradiation produces stable dispersions with sulphatides but cerebrosides apparently are not dispersible in water.

Biological Relevance

As with the phosphoglycerides, the sphingolipid molecules contain within themselves hydrophobic and hydrophilic properties causing them to orient themselves spontaneously in water. This property is probably important for their rôle in the formation of biological membranes. It can be seen from Table 4.1 in the previous chapter, that these lipids occur in myelin and erythrocyte membranes.

The lipids derived from glycerol are rapidly metabolized and their component parts readily utilized either anabolically or catabolically. The sphingosine-containing lipids appear to be metabolized slowly giving sphingosine which is metabolized slowly. This may correspond with the idea that the sphingolipids are concerned as structural components in those parts of the cells which demand stability, e.g., the myelin sheath, whilst the glycerides are concerned in storage in adipose tissue or in structures where the turnover of components is more rapid, e.g., plasma membranes.

The rôle of the fatty acid chains present in these lipids is probably similar to the rôle they play in the phosphoglycerides, i.e., to provide the correct degree of hydrophobic character and perhaps also the correct amount of fluidity for the membrane. The fatty acids in the myelin membranes are more saturated than those found in, say, the phosphoglycerides of mitochondrial membranes. This may be because of the stability requirements for the myelin membranes. The lipids in the myelin membranes are not metabolized in adult life in the normal animal. A reduction in the fatty acid chain length occurs in these lipids corresponding to certain diseases.

There are three diseases affecting the distribution of sphingolipids. In the condition termed Niemann–Pick disease large pale cells are observed containing large quantities of sphingomyelin. These cells are particularly concentrated in the spleen. The disease occurs in infants during the first year of life and is fatal.

A second disease, referred to as Tay–Sachs disease, causes congenital idiocy in the new-born and is generally fatal. Whilst the amount of sphingomyelin remains normal, the amount of gangliosides in the brain is greatly increased. There is also a partial corresponding reduction in the content of brain cerebrosides. It is thought that the gangliosides in this disease are of abnormal constitution.

A third disease, known as Gaucher's disease, causes the spleen to become enormously enlarged due to the accumulation of Gaucher cells. These cells are heavily laden with an unusual type of cerebroside containing only glucose instead of the typical predominantly galactose content of normal spleen cerebrosides.

There are also diseases referred to as leucodystrophies (familial diffuse scleroses). These are inherited and are characterized by a progressive degeneration of white matter. In late infantile metachromatic leucodystrophy there is an accumulation of the cerebroside sulphatides. The lipids of the grey matter appear to remain normal.

Various other disorders of the nervous system in which lipids are involved are also known. Metabolic disorders which prevent the normal deposition of myelin during development, or cause its destruction in adult life, are receiving considerable attention.

Complex lipids which contain a ceramide moiety, i.e., a long-chain fatty, N-acyl derivative of the base sphingosine as a common portion of their structure, appear to have immunogenic properties. Structurally related ceramide polyhexosides of erythrocytes are responsible for the antigenicity of blood groups A and B. Rabbits injected with suspensions of organs of guinea pigs and some other animals produce antibodies which cause the lysis of sheep erythrocytes. The component responsible for the specificity of the antigen is soluble in alcohol and is very weakly antigenic. Alcoholic extracts of the spirochete *Trepanema pallidum*, as well as alcoholic extracts of normal organs, were found to work very well as sources of the Wasserman antigen in the complement fixation reaction for the serological diagnosis of syphilis.

Although ceramides themselves are non-haptenic, they acquire haptenic properties when various carbohydrate residues are glycosidically linked to the hydroxyl group of the sphingosine. The material responsible is a glycosphingolipid containing one molecule each of sphingosine, fatty acid, glucose, and galactose. It is now generally referred to as ceramide dihexoside or ceramide lactose.

Galactocerebroside is also a hapten. It is thought that this is the essential component involved in the production of brain-specific antibodies. With the exception of materials such as cardiolipin and simple alcohol-soluble toxic materials like urushiol, all lipid haptens appear to contain at least one molecule of a sugar covalently linked to the residual lipid portion of the molecule. Psychosine, the product obtained by deacylation of cerebrosides, see page 108, is fully anti-genic when coupled with a protein through diazotization of its N-p-aminobenzoyl derivative. The lack of haptenic function of non-carbohydrate-containing lipids seems well established. How-ever, antibody reactions to lipid haptens are markedly enhanced by the addition of various other lipids *in vitro*. The effects of auxiliary lipids such as lecithin and cholesterol seem particularly pronounced in the complement fixation tests for cardiolipin and ceramide lactose.

Immunochemical studies with lipids may provide insight into the etiology of various demyelinating conditions. The presence of anticeramide lactose antibody activity in normal human serum may, in some fashion, be related to a natural immunity to certain forms of cancer. In the field of rheumatic heart disease, research has led to the question whether the antibody produced against streptococcal cell wall material can cross-react with mammalian heart tissue.

Further reading

General

D. J. Hanahan and G. A. Thompson, *Ann. Rev. Biochem.*, **32**, 215 (1963).
H. E. Carter, P. Johnson, and E. J. Weber, *Ann. Rev. Biochem.*, **34**, 109 (1965).
I. H. Goldberg, *J. Lipid Research*, **2**, 103 (1961).
R. M. Burton, *Lipids and Lipidoses* (ed. G. Schettler). Springer-Verlag, 1967.
J. Polonovski, *Bull. Soc. Chim. Biol.*, **46**, 833 (1964).
N. S. Radin, *Lipids*, **1**, 47 (1966).
R. O. Brady and E. C. Trams, *Ann. Rev. Biochem.*, **33**, 75 (1964).

Gangliosides

R. Ledeen, *J. Am. Oil Chem. Soc.*, **43**, 57 (1966).
L. Svennerholm, *J. Lipid Research*, **5**, 145 (1964).

Lipids and the brain

J. Folch-Pi and H. J. Bauer (ed.), *Brain Lipids and Lipoproteins and the Leucodystrophies*. Elsevier, 1963.
H. McIlwain, *Chemical Exploration of the Brain*. Elsevier, 1963.

Physical Properties

D. B. Gammack, J. H. Perrin, and L. Saunders, *Biochim. Biophys. Acta*, **84**, 576 (1964).

R. E. Howard and R. M. Burton, *Biochim. Biophys. Acta*, **84**, 435 (1964).

F. Reiss-Husson, *J. Mol. Biol.*, **25**, 363 (1967).

6. Some Glycolipids

Complex lipids which contain carbohydrates are often generally referred to as glycolipids. Some of the lipids mentioned in the chapter on phosphoglycerides could be called glycolipids. A number of the sphingosine lipids could also have been included under this general heading. We have preferred to discuss these lipids under the phosphoglyceride and sphingosine grouping. In the present chapter we shall discuss some glycosyl glycerides which occur in plant systems.

Structure and Occurrence

Glycosyl glycerides occur in plants and algae mainly in chloroplasts and also in bacteria.* They do not seem to accumulate in mitochondria. Monogalactosyl diglyceride and digalactosyl diglyceride were first isolated from the lipids of wheat flour.

The structures of these molecules are shown:

---

* Recently (Lennarz) the structure and biosynthesis of several bacterial glycolipids have been reported.

The mono- and digalactosyl diglycerides isolated from runner-bean leaves show high linolenic acid content, 96 and 93 per cent respectively. In spinach leaves the monogalactosyl diglyceride contains 67 per cent linolenic acid, whilst the digalactosyl diglyceride contains 84 per cent linolenic acid. The linolenic acid content of glycolipids from algal sources, however, rarely exceeds 20 per cent.

In chloroplasts kept in the dark, the monogalactosyl diglyceride decreases appreciably. Exposure to darkness of bean leaf plastids results in a higher proportion of saturated fatty acids. Light-induced greening of *Euglena gracilis* causes a linear increase of the glycosyl-glyceride content. Illumination of well nourished etiolated cells produces a rapid disappearance of the major C_{13} and C_{14} saturated acids which are replaced by unsaturated fatty acids, mainly of the C_{16} and C_{18} series. These acids account for about 80 per cent of the total lipids of plant systems.

A sulphur glycolipid has been found in plants and photosynthetic algae. This lipid and phosphatidyl glycerol derivatives each provide about 10 per cent of the total-plant lipid. The structure of this sulpholipid is shown.

The plant sulpholipid has been found in all photosynthetic plants, algae, and bacteria yet investigated. Its concentration approximates those of the major phosphatides. Other photosynthetic protozoa, *Euglena* and *Chlamydomonas*, contain high concentrations of sulpholipid.

The sulpholipid appears to be concentrated in the lamellar membranes of the chloroplasts of plants. Spinach chloroplasts contain 73 per cent of the leaf sulpholipid and 79 per cent of the leaf galactolipids in contrast to only 28 per cent of the leaf phosphatides. Although little or no sulpholipid occurs in seeds, its concentration in photosynthetic tissues of most plants is 1 to 6 × 10^{-3} M and approximates that of phosphatidylcholine. Fresh or field-dried alfalfa or clover are good sources of sulpholipid. Highest concentrations were observed in the marine red algae. Recent reports indicate a rapid synthesis and turnover of sulphur lipid in response to illumination and respiratory activity. Hence, figures for its concentration in plant tissues may be re-evaluated when its role in sulphur and carbohydrate metabolism is clearly delineated.

The properties of the sulpholipid are consistent with a high linolenate complement. Alfalfa leaf sulpholipid has been found (O'Brien, 1963) to contain 47 per cent octadecatrienoic acid, 43 per cent (67 per cent in *Chlorella*) palmitic acid, 4 per cent octadecadienoic acid, 3 per cent stearic acid, and 2 per cent (18 per cent in *Chlorella*) octadecenoic acid. Positions of the saturated and unsaturated fatty acid esters on the glycerol have not yet been determined.

Table 6.1. Lipid molar ratios (relative to sulpholipid)

	Anacystis nidulans	Spinach lamellae	Spinach chloroplast	*Chlorella*
Monogalactosyl diglyceride	32	36	80	92
Digalactosyl diglyceride	12	20	33	38
Phosphatidyl glycerol	9	14	9	33
Sulpholipid	10	10	10	10
Lecithin	—	5	8	15
Phosphatidyl-inositol	—	3	3	8
Phosphatidyl-ethanolamine	—	—	0·3	6

Biological Relevance

The distribution of lipids in various plant systems is given in Table 6.1. A complete understanding of the rôle which these plant glycolipids play in these systems is not yet available. Possible functions for these lipids include (a) metabolic links in electron transfer processes involved in photosynthesis; (b) a structural component for holding pigment molecules in specific arrays; (c) areas of low dielectric constant; (d) metabolic links in lipid biosynthesis.

Because α-linolenic acid is a primary constituent of chloroplast lipids, it has been suggested that it is a necessary component for photosynthesis and for one or more steps leading to oxygen evolution. It has also been suggested that the linolenic acids have a specific requirement in chloroplast lipoproteins. However, glycolipids from the chloroplasts of *Anacystis nidulans* contain no linolenic acid, nor any other polyenoic fatty acid, yet photosynthesis and the Hill reaction take place.

When digalactosyl dilinolenin is placed in water it forms stable myelin figures. During the preparation of fragmented leaf sections for microscopy myelin figures are observed.

The sulpholipid is among the most concentrated anionic sugar derivative in plants. As a salt of a very strong sulphonic acid, it is anionic under all conditions. The sulpholipid possesses an extremely hydrophilic moiety as well as its two fatty ester groups. This amphipathic molecule is expected to exhibit marked surface-active properties. Its high concentration in the lamellar lipoprotein structures of plant chloroplasts is probably a result of such properties. Its rôle in sulphate reduction and carbohydrate metabolism is not yet clearly understood, but it may be related to its location and orientation at important interfaces in the photosynthetic apparatus.

Further reading

General

A. A. Benson, *Advances in Lipid Research*, Vol. 1, p. 387, Academic Press, 1963.
A. A. Benson, H. Daniel, and R. Wiser, *Proc. Nat. Acad. Sci.*, **45**, 1582 (1959).
H. E. Carter, R. A. Hendry, and N. Z. Stanacer, *J. Lipid Research*, **2**, 223 (1961).

Rôle in Plant Membrane Systems

A. A. Benson, *Ann. Rev. Plant Physiol.*, **15**, 1 (1964).
T. W. Goodwin (ed.), *Biochemistry of Chloroplasts*, Academic Press, 1966.

Bacteria

W. J. Lennarz, *Advances in Lipid Research*, Vol. 4, p. 175, Academic Press, 1966.

7. The Role of Lipids in Biology

Unanswered Questions

In the preceding pages we have tried to indicate what may be the possible biological relevance of lipid molecules. In this final chapter we shall try to pick out a few of the important and, as yet, unanswered questions concerning lipids. There are, of course, many other questions than the ones which we shall discuss, but these appear to be among the more important ones at the present time.

Perhaps the most outstanding area of uncertainty at present concerns the way in which lipids and proteins interact. This is of considerable importance for understanding membrane structure and also for understanding a variety of enzyme reactions. In the developing membrane of cells it is not known whether the protein structure guides adsorption of the lipid molecules, or whether the lipids direct the orientation and conformation of the protein. How the protein interacts, whether mainly by means of the polar group of the lipid, or whether it is by hydrophobic interaction between the hydrocarbon chains of the lipid and the protein is also uncertain. At present there is little experimental information available to enable us to decide between the two possibilities, and it may be that different membrane types involve each of these modes of interaction. There are many membrane models based essentially on these two alternative methods of interaction.

Even if it were agreed that the simple bilayer model of a membrane is the correct description or even the dominant structure, there are still many questions concerning membranes which remain unanswered, e.g., why are different lipid classes, such as the lecithins, phosphatidylethanolamines, etc., present in membranes? What determines the ratio of one class to another? Can one type of lipid substitute for another? Is it a question of retaining the correct

Lipid bilayer   Protein   New lipoprotein
                                    arrangement

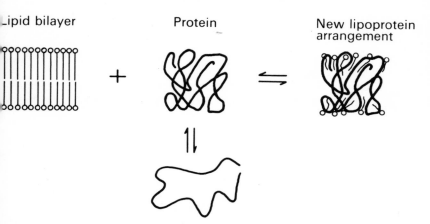

Fig. 7.1. A schematic diagram showing the dynamic interaction
between the phospholipid bilayer and protein giving rise to a new
structural arrangement of lipid and protein which may occur in some
membranes

charge requirements of the membrane or some other factor? Are
the various lipid classes laid down in some special code or order,
determined perhaps by protein configuration, or are they all mixed
in a membrane in a random manner?

We have seen in the early chapters that the fatty acids associated
with lipids, including the simple glycerides, phospholipids, and
complex lipids, always have a distribution of chain length and
unsaturation. What are the reasons for having this distribution? Is
the particular combination of chain length and unsaturation which
occurs in a membrane important only in preserving the correct
liquid fluidity of the membrane or the correct liquid–crystalline
phase in the membrane? Why when a poikilothermic organism is
reared at different temperatures does the amount of unsaturation
present in the hydrocarbon chains of the lipids vary? Is this merely
the direct result of the effect of temperature on the biosynthetic
mechanism, or is it related more subtly with fluidity requirements?

As we discussed in chapter 3, cholesterol is present in many but
not all membranes. Despite much speculation we are still not clear
as to its main purpose in membranes and the reason why it is
present in some membranes but not in others. Even at the molecular
level the precise way in which phospholipid molecules can interact

with the cholesterol molecule is still unclear. There are many theoretical models and publications discussing this interaction. As yet, there is insufficient experimental evidence to be completely convincing.

When we consider the particular functions of biological membranes there are also many questions which require resolution. Are some of the lipids present in the membrane specifically to determine the transport of ions or other molecules through the membrane, e.g., are phosphatidic acids, or any other phospholipids, involved in the sodium pump mechanism? Alternatively do the lipids merely provide a general matrix capable of organizing enzymes which are themselves the important transport control entities? Membranes are important for organizing molecules, such as chlorophyll in plant systems, and also for organizing retinene in the eye. Whether this organizational effect springs from the lipid class or from the type of fatty acid present is unclear. How specific the lipid requirements are for this purpose is unknown. The reason for the combination of both lipid and sugar groups which occur in the glycolipids is also not understood. The action of hormones, drugs, anaesthetics, and indeed, a great deal of sensory response, such as the senses of smell and taste, appear to be triggered at membrane surfaces. It is still uncertain whether the lipids are involved in a passive or an active way in these interactions.

When we consider the relevance of lipids to medicine and disease there are also many unresolved questions, e.g., are saturated fatty acids really more harmful in the diet than unsaturated fatty acids and, if so, why? Is the major rôle of the so-called essential fatty acids to act as precursors of the prostaglandins or do they have other important functions as well? The process of demyelination is one at present receiving attention, and there are many speculations about its causes. Finally, the area of brain research is producing many questions. What do we know of the specific rôle of lipids which occur in the brain; is it in an active or a passive rôle? Are lipids involved in some way in memory processes?

These are only a few of an almost unending list of unanswered questions which are at present puzzling lipid chemists, biochemists, biologists, and biophysicists. The study of lipid molecules has, therefore, acquired a much more urgent and important rôle than ever before in the history of the subject. There are very many speculations and theoretical models purporting to show the real biological function of lipids but much more experimental research is required. It is hoped that this short text will stimulate some readers to try to solve these questions.

Further reading

General

A. A. Benson, *J. Amer. Oil Chem. Soc.*, **43**, 265 (1966).

K. Bloch, *Evolving Genes Proteins*, Symposium Rutgers State University, 1964, p. 53–65 (published 1965).

D. Chapman, The Structure of Biological Membranes, *Science Journal*, **4**, No. 3, 55 (1968).

D. Chapman (ed.), *Biological Membranes*, Academic Press, 1968.

D. E. Green and A. Tzagoloff, *J. Lipid Res.*, **7**, 587 (1966).

E. D. Korn, *Science*, **153**, 1491 (1966).

Appendix

The following nomenclature of lipids is from a document for discussion, sponsored by the IUPAC-IUB Commission on Biochemical Nomenclature, approved by the Commission in April 1967, and published by permission of the International Union of Biochemistry, and the official publishers of the International Union of Pure and Applied Chemistry, Messrs. Butterworths Scientific Publications.

Proposed Rules

1. Lipids Containing Glycerol

A. Individual compounds

1.1. In designating esters, ethers, and other O-derivatives of glycerol, rules 10 and 11 of the Rules of Carbohydrate Nomenclature [*J. Org. Chem.* 28 (1963) 281] are followed. These rules provide that: (a) if the hydrogen atom of an alcoholic hydroxyl group is replaced by another atom or group, the name of the parent compound may be retained as the root of the substituted compound and that, in such names, the prefix (denoting the substituent) is attached directly to the root; (b) an ester may be named by placing after the unchanged name of the parent compound, and separated therefrom by a space, the appropriate numeral (indicating position) and a hyphen, as prefix to the name of the anionic group derived from an acid.

If the substitution is on the carbon atom, the compound is designated by its systematic name and not as a derivative of glycerol. It is permissible, therefore, to omit the symbol 'O' if the substitution is on the oxygen atoms of glycerol.

Examples. Glycerol tristearate, or tristearoylglycerol, or tri-O-stearoylglycerol; 1,3-benzylideneglycerol or 1,3-O-benzylidene-glycerol; glycerol 2-(dihydrogen phosphate) (a permissible alternative to this term is 'glycero-2-phosphoric acid').

1.2. In order to designate the stereochemistry of glycerol derivatives, the carbon atoms of glycerol are numbered stereospecifically. The carbon atom that appears on top in that Fischer projection that shows a vertical carbon chain with the secondary hydroxyl group to the left is designated as C-1. To differentiate such numbering from conventional numbering conveying no steric information, the prefix '*sn*' (for *s*tereospecifically *n*umbered) is used. This term is printed in lowercase italics, even at the beginning of a sentence, and it immediately precedes the term signifying glycerol and is separated from it by a hyphen. The prefix '*rac-*' (for racemo) precedes the full name if the product is an equal mixture of both antipodes, and the prefix '*X-*' if the configuration of the compound is either unknown or unspecified.

Examples. *sn*-Glycerol 3-(dihydrogen phosphate) or *sn*-glycero-3-phosphoric acid for the stereoisomer previously known as either L-α-glycerophosphoric acid [E. Baer and H. O. L. Fischer, *J. Biol. Chem.* 128 (1939) 491] or as D-glycerol 1-phosphate [A. A. Benson and B. Maruo, *Biochim. Biophys. Acta*, 27 (1958) 189]; *rac*-1-hexadecylglycerol; *X*-glycerol 1,2-dipalmitate 3-stearate.

B. Generic terms

1.3. The term 'phosphoglyceride' signifies any derivative of glycerophosphoric acid that contains at least one *O*-acyl, or *O*-alkyl, or *O*-alk-1'-en-1'-yl group attached to the glycerol residue. If the other ester component of a phosphoglyceride is known, it can be stated in a word that precedes the generic term.

Example. Choline phosphoglyceride.

1.4. The term 'phosphatidic acid' signifies a derivative of glycerophosphoric acid in which both remaining hydroxyl groups of glycerol are esterified with fatty acids.

1.5. The term 'lecithin' is permitted but not recommended to designate a 1,2-diacyl-*sn*-glycero-3-phosphorylcholine. The recommended generic term for such compounds is 3-*sn*-phosphatidylcholine.

1.6. Other generic terms may be coined as needed. These should be patterned after the names of individual compounds (see 1A) and should indicate the type of substituent of glycerol by such prefixes as acyl, alkyl or alkenyl (for alk-1'-en-1'-yl, i.e., R—CH=CH—). If the nature of these substituents cannot be specified, the prefix 'radyl' may be used.

Examples for rules 1.4 and 1.6: phosphatidic ester; 1-alkenyl-2-acyl-*sn*-glycerophosphoric ester; *O*-(diradylglycerophosphoryl)-L-serine; *O*-(1-acyl-*sn*-glycero-3-phosphoryl)-ethanolamine; triacylglycerol; diacyl-*sn*-glycero-3-phosphoryl-1'-*sn*-glycerol or 3-*sn*-phosphatidyl-1'-*sn*-glycerol for structure (IX).

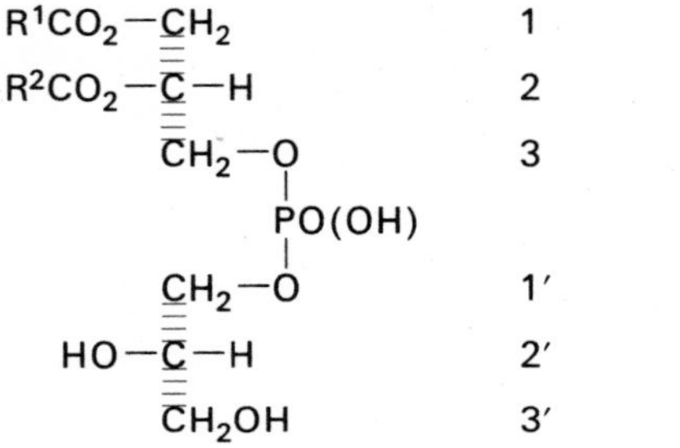

$$
\begin{array}{ll}
R^1CO_2-CH_2 & 1 \\
R^2CO_2-C-H & 2 \\
CH_2-O & 3 \\
\quad\quad\ | & \\
\quad\ PO(OH) & \\
\quad\quad\ | & \\
CH_2-O & 1' \\
HO-C-H & 2' \\
CH_2OH & 3'
\end{array}
$$

(*sn*-numbering)
3-*sn*-phosphatidyl-1'-*sn*-glycerol
IX

Comment. The terms triacylglycerol, diacylglycerol are preferred for neutral fats, not only for consistency, but mainly because strict interpretation of the traditional (optional) terms triglyceride, diglyceride does not convey the intended meaning.

2. Sphingolipids

A. Individual compounds

The discovery of many compounds structurally related to sphingosine makes it desirable to develop a semi-systematic nomenclature affording more concise names than the general rules of organic-chemical nomenclature.

2.1. The compound previously known as dihydrosphingosine [2D-aminoöctadecane-1,3D-diol or D-*erythro*-2-aminoöctadecane-1,3-diol or (2S, 3R)-2-aminoöctadecane-1,3-diol] is called sphinganine.

2.2. This name may be modified by prefixes to indicate additional substituents or higher or lower homologues. The prefixes to designate homologues should be derived by deleting the terminal 'ne' from the systematic names of the hydrocarbons [IUPAC

Nomenclature of Organic Chemistry 1957, *J. Am. Chem. Soc.* 82 (1960) 5545, Rule A-1] that have the same number of carbon atoms as the long-chain bases.

2.3. The configuration of additional substituents should be specified by the prefixes '*D*-' or '*L*-' [italic capitals, cf. J. A. Mills and W. Klyne, *Progress in Stereochemistry*, 1 (1954) 181] following the number that indicates the position of the substituted carbon atom. The configurations at C-2 and C-3 should be specified in the same manner, but only if they differ from those in sphinganine. In every case, the prefixes *D* or *L* refer to the orientation of the functional groups to the right or left, respectively, of the carbon chain written vertically in a Fischer projection with C-1 on top. If the configuration is unknown, the prefix '*X*-' should be used. In the case of racemic mixtures, the term '*rac*-' should be used as a prefix to the name.

Comment. The semisystematic nomenclature of the long-chain bases is significantly shorter than fully systematic names only if the terms chosen imply not only substituents but also their configurations. The configurations usually encountered have identical configurational prefixes only if a *D/L* but not if the *R/S* system is used; e.g., C-3 is *D* and *R* in sphingosine and *D* and *S* in the compound previously known as phytosphingosine. Therefore, the rule that configurations at C-2 and C-3 are to be specified only if they differ from those in sphinganine is unambiguous only if the *D/L* system is used. Whenever it is desired to use the *R/S* system [R. S. Cahn, C. K. Ingold and V. Prelog, *Angew. Chemie* (international edition), 5 (1966) 385] the fully systematic names should be used with specification of configuration at every centre (and, when applicable, of the geometry at the double bond).

2.4. Names for partly unsaturated compounds are derived from the names of the corresponding saturated compounds by terminations denoting unsaturation, namely 'ene', 'diene', 'yne', etc. A double bond is presumed to have the *trans* orientation of the carbon chain unless *cis* or unknown geometry is specified by the terms 'cis-' or '*x*-' preceding the number that indicates the position of the double bond.

Examples for rules 2.1 to 2.4: 4*D*-hydroxysphinganine for phytosphingosine; 4*X*-hydroxy-2*X*,3*X*-eicosasphinganine for the cerebrin base described by M. Prostenik and N. Z. Stanačev [*Chem. Ber.* 91 (1958) 961]; 4-sphingenine for sphingosine; *cis*-4-sphingenine for the geometric isomer of sphingosine; 2L-sphinganine for the C-2 epimer of sphinganine.

2.5. The trivial name 'sphingosine' may be retained. If trivial names other than sphingosine are used, they should be defined in each paper in terms of this nomenclature, or of the general nomenclature of organic chemistry.

B. Generic terms

Definition. The term 'long-chain base' as used in section 2 refers to sphinganine, its homologues and stereoisomers, and to the hydroxy and unsaturated derivatives of these compounds.

2.6. The following generic terms may be used for the following groups of compounds:

— sphingolipid, for any lipid containing a long-chain base;
— glycosphingolipid, for any lipid containing a long-chain base and one or more sugars;
— ceramide, for an *N*-acyl long-chain base;
— cerebroside, for a monoglycosylceramide;
— ganglioside, for a glycosphingolipid containing neuraminic acid (see Section 3);
— sphingomyelin, for a ceramide 1-phosphorylcholine.

2.7. If further structural details can be specified, appropriate prefixes should be used. These prefixes signify substitution and not definition or modification of a component already implied in the root name.

Examples. 1-*O*-D-galactosylceramide, but not galactosecerebroside; *N*-acyl-1-*O*-D-galactosyl-4-sphingenine, if the structure of the long-chain base can also be specified; 1-triglycosylceramide, oligoglycosylceramide.

3. Neuraminic Acid

3.1. The compound 5-amino-3,5-dideoxy-D-*glycero*-D-*galacto*-nonulosonic acid is neuraminic acid (X).

3.2. The term 'sialic acid' signifies the *N*-acylneuraminic acids and their esters and other derivatives of the alcoholic hydroxyl groups.

3.3. The radicals resulting from the deletion of a hydroxyl group of neuraminic acid of sialic acid are designated as neuraminoyl or sialoyl, respectively, if the hydroxyl is deleted from the carboxyl group, and as neuraminosyl and sialosyl, respectively, if the hydroxyl group is removed from the anomeric carbon atom of the cyclic structure.

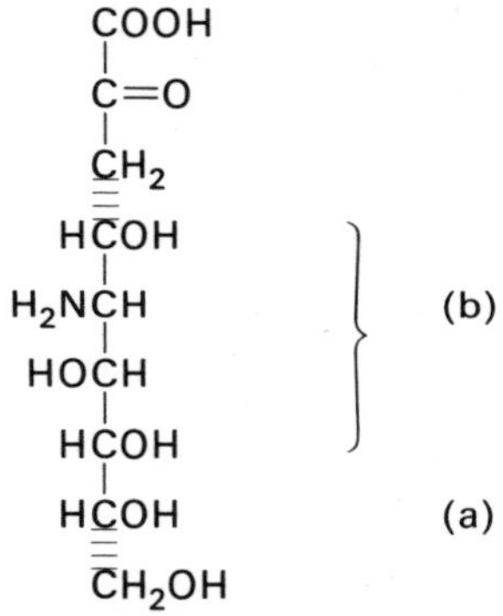

$$
\begin{array}{l}
\text{COOH} \\
|\\
\text{C}=\text{O} \\
|\\
\text{CH}_2 \\
|\\
\text{HCOH} \\
|\\
\text{H}_2\text{NCH} \\
|\\
\text{HOCH} \\
|\\
\text{HCOH} \\
|\\
\text{HCOH} \\
|\\
\text{CH}_2\text{OH}
\end{array}
$$

(b)

(a)

Neuraminic acid
5-Amino-3,5-dideoxy-D-*glycero*-D-*galacto*-nonulosonic acid
(a)   (b)

X

4. Other Components of Lipids

4.1. Fatty acids and their radicals should be named according to the IUPAC rules for the Nomenclature of Organic Chemistry [*Pure and Applied Chem.*, 11 (1965) Nos. 1–2], Rule C-4. Fatty acids should always be numbered with the carboxyl group as C-1.

Comment. Regularities, such as the position of double bonds in some naturally occurring fatty acids, that are not apparent if numbering is done in this manner, can be indicated without violation of this principle of numbering if the position of the double bond is stated in the form $(n\text{-}x)$ where n indicates the number of carbon atoms in the chain. The positions of the double bonds of linoleic acid, e.g., may be given as $(n\text{-}9)$ and $(n\text{-}6)$ but not as $\omega 9$, $\omega 6$.

4.2. Long-chain alcohols and the radicals derived from them should be designated according to systematic nomenclature [*loc. cit.* in 4.1, Rule C-201; also *J. Am. Chem. Soc.* 82 (1960), 5545, Rule A-1 *et seq.*] but not by trivial names that are derived from those of fatty acids.

Example. 1-Hexadecanol and 1-hexadecyl, but not palmityl alcohol and palmityl.

4.3. Other components of lipids, such as amino acids and sugars, should be named according to the internationally adopted conventions for these groups of compounds.

4.4. All trivial names or abbreviations that are not defined in the rules of sections 1–4 or the other rules cited should be defined in each paper.

5. Other Generic Terms

5.1. The term 'phospholipid' may be used for any lipid containing a radical derived from phosphoric acid.

5.2. The term 'phosphoinositide' may be used for any lipid containing radicals derived from inositol and phosphoric acid.

5.3. Synonyms for the generic terms defined in these rules should not be used, but other terms may be employed if they apply to different groups of lipids. Such non-official generic terms should be defined in each paper and should be so constructed that prefixes denote substituting groups rather than define components already implied in the root name.

Index

1 2

Date Due

MAY 0 7 2001			

CAT. NO. 23 233   PRINTED IN U.S.A.